Cherish wanted to kick him. "Please, don't—"

"No, really," Ziggy insisted mischievously. "I don't normally get, you know, like *this* after only two or three kisses."

"You remember something?" Her face flushed with heat, but she doggedly continued. "You remember doing—" she cleared her throat "—something?"

Ziggy drew in a quick breath and propped himself up on his good elbow, his face alert and serious.

"For a moment," he murmured, "I had a . . . I don't know. There were familiar feelings. Touching a woman, making love. I felt like I'd done it before. Like I had a lot of . . . previous experience." He glanced up at Cherish. "What was your impression, Doc? Did I seem like I knew what I was doing?"

"Maybe your memory will start to return after you've had a little more rest." Cherish's voice was crisp and schoolmarmish.

"Or we could fool around a little more. See if it stimulates things."

Dear Reader:

Welcome to Silhouette Desire – provocative, compelling, contemporary love stories written by and for today's woman. These are stories to treasure.

Each and every Silhouette Desire is a wonderful romance in which the emotional and the sensual go hand in hand. When you open a Desire, you enter a whole new world – a world that has, naturally, a perfect hero just waiting to whisk you away! A Silhouette Desire can be light-hearted or serious, but it will always be satisfying.

We hope you enjoy this Desire today – and will go on to enjoy many more.

Please write to us:

Jane Nicholls
Silhouette Books
PO Box 236
Thornton Road
Croydon
Surrey
CR9 3RU

LAURA LEONE

UNDER THE VOODOO MOON

Silhouette Desire

Originally Published by Silhouette Books
a division of
Harlequin Enterprises Ltd.

*All the characters in this book have no existence outside the imagination of
the Author, and have no relation whatsoever to anyone bearing the same
name or names. They are not even distantly inspired by any individual
known or unknown to the Author, and all the incidents are pure invention.*

*First published in Great Britain in 1994
by Silhouette Books, Eton House, 18-24 Paradise Road,
Richmond, Surrey TW9 1SR*

© Laura Resnick 1994

*Silhouette, Silhouette Desire and Colophon are
Trade Marks of Harlequin Enterprises B.V.*

ISBN 0 373 59238 8

22-9406

Made and printed in Great Britain

LAURA LEONE

believes in double-fudge brownies, hypnotism before exams, living out of a backpack, the power of the written word, earthly delights and the small of a man's back. This award-winning author has studied languages in Washington D.C., acting in London, human nature in New York and urban-survival skills in the streets of Palermo. The daughter of a prominent science-fiction writer, she is alternately proud and alarmed to be carrying on the family tradition.

Other Silhouette Books by Laura Leone

Silhouette Desire

One Sultry Summer
A Wilder Name
Ulterior Motives
Guilty Secrets
Upon a Midnight Clear
Celestial Bodies
The Black Sheep
Untouched by Man

Silhouette Special Edition

A Woman's Work
The Bandit King

For Jim and Joyce Ferree,
adventurers in Central America

One

She found him at dawn, lying facedown on the smooth, wet sand, so close to the water that it washed up over his legs with every rhythmic wave. As she walked along the shore's edge, she was so intent upon the early-morning light glittering on the Caribbean Sea, which swelled and undulated majestically in the wake of last night's violent storm, that she tripped over his prostrate form.

"Oh!" She scrambled gracelessly as her legs got tangled up with his, then fell on top of him with a force that probably hurt him more than it hurt her. "Oof!"

"Hey, Doc!" Luke Martinez cried from fifty yards away, his voice a thin echo borne on the wind. As usual, he wasn't able to keep up with her long strides and was therefore far behind her.

She rolled over, disentangling herself from the motionless form beneath her, and drew in a gasping breath. "What on earth..."

"Hey, Doc!" Luke had broken into a run and was hurtling toward her.

"Oh, my God," she breathed, panic chilling her blood the moment she took a good look at the obstacle that had brought her down.

"Doc, are you okay?" Luke shouted, bearing down on her.

"Oh, my God," she repeated, staring in horror at the unconscious man. His battered face was turned toward her, and his eyes were closed.

"*Santa Maria!*" Luke's eyes widened as he came to an abrupt halt. After a brief moment, he said disapprovingly, "I told you not to come down here alone before the sun was high."

She glanced up at her small companion. All of ten years old, Luke had insisted on coming along to protect her from all sorts of horrors—pirate ghosts, sea monsters, black butterflies, the Greasy Man, the Ashi de Pompi, *duendes* and deadly snakes. But *this* was something she doubted he had imagined even in his wildest dreams, since strangers almost never came to Voodoo Caye.

"Is he dead?" Luke breathed.

"I don't know." Her instinctive need to help the stranger conflicted with her primitive dread of touching a dead man. Her PhD didn't qualify her to deal with a situation like this.

"Well?" Luke prodded.

She bit her lip and searched for the man's pulse, brushing trembling fingers along his throat. Her breath caught with relief when she felt the strong, steady beat of blood pounding through his veins and arteries. "He's alive!"

"Who is he? How did he get here?"

"I don't know." The stranger wore a life preserver around his neck, which caused his entire upper body to lie at a peculiar angle. He was clutching something in his left arm, but it was trapped under his body, so she couldn't tell what it was. "He must have washed up on shore during the storm," she said. The waves had pounded the eastern shore for hours, bringing all manner of flotsam and jetsam to the island. "He's lucky to be alive."

"He can't be very smart," Luke said critically. "To swim or sail during a storm—"

"I doubt he planned it that way. Help me turn him over."

They seized his shoulder and pulled, an action that produced a surprisingly loud groan from someone who hadn't even appeared to be breathing a moment ago. With some effort, they managed to remove the life preserver and roll him onto his back.

"Doc!" Luke exclaimed.

She was too shocked to say anything, although she didn't know which revelation stunned her more—the stuffed bunny rabbit that the stranger held in a virtual death grip, or the bloody wound on his left shoulder, which, if she was not mistaken, had been made by a knife.

"That's no shark bite," Luke said.

"No." She pushed aside the torn and red-smeared rags of the man's shirt to assess the wound. She must have hurt him, for he flinched and groaned again. Suddenly his dark eyelashes fluttered open and, a moment later, she was staring into eyes as gray and depthless as the dawning, storm-tossed sky above them.

Realizing the distress he must feel at this moment, she said. "You're safe. Don't worry, you're perfectly safe now."

She saw the way relief softened his masculine features for a moment. Then, with great effort, he said something. His voice was so weak that she had to lean very close to hear him. Her long red hair brushed his cheek and her full breasts pressed against his right shoulder.

"What?" she asked.

He swallowed with obvious difficulty and tried again. His voice was stronger this time. "Who are you?"

"I'm Cherish Love."

He stared at her for a moment. Then, to her surprise, a wry and astonishingly sensual smile stole slowly across his bruised face. "You sure as hell are," he murmured a moment before he passed out again.

Cherish sent Luke into the village, and he returned ten minutes later with a couple of his relatives, both tall, broad-shouldered Garifuna fishermen with the coffee-brown skin of their African ancestors. Cherish had the impression that they tolerantly regarded the unconscious stranger's sudden appearance on their island as being simply another one of her little eccentricities. Lifting the stranger as easily as if he were a bag of feed, they carried him back to the simple two-room cabin at the edge of the village that Cherish rented from Luke's grandfather.

"He's going to need a lot of work," Cherish told Luke as the men left her cabin. "I'll need your grandmother's help."

"I will find her," Luke promised, then scurried off again.

Left alone with the stranger, Cherish looked down at him as he lay sprawled across her bed. She scowled slightly when she noticed that his sand-caked, salt water-soaked, wounded body was already doing irrevocable damage to her only set of sheets. While the Martinez men had hauled him here, she had carried his life preserver and stuffed bunny. Still holding the rabbit gingerly by its ear—the only part of it she was willing to touch—she regarded the thing with considerable disfavor; its cheap pink dye was running, and it had dripped on her sensible, pale blouse. She deposited the toy atop a tidy pile of last month's newspapers, then she leaned the life preserver against the wall. According to the faded lettering on its scarred surface, the stranger had come from a boat called the *Lusty Wench*.

"Probably not a Navy vessel," she muttered sardonically, leaving the bedroom and entering the main room. Could the *Lusty Wench* be a yacht? A dinghy? A cruise ship?

Although there was no electricity anywhere on Voodoo Caye, Cherish's cabin did have running water. There was even *hot* water available, thanks to a clever—though probably highly flammable—system of gas tanks, which were replaced every few weeks. Since the stranger obviously needed considerable cleaning up, Cherish started filling a bucket with hot water and searched for some clean rags. Then she hauled the supplies back into the bedroom and stood over the bed, studying her unexpected guest.

He had taken a real beating, in addition to the wound on his shoulder. There was a deep, nasty scratch running down the whole right side of his face, his left eye was blackened and there were swelling bruises on his cheek and jaw. None of these heartbreaking signs of suffering, however, could hide the fact that he was a very handsome man.

His face was strong and aristocratic, with a square jaw, prominent cheekbones, a straight nose and a wide, sensual mouth. The dark stubble on his face made her guess that he hadn't shaved for a couple of days, but everything else about him suggested that he was usually well-groomed. His wavy, chestnut-brown hair was neatly trimmed, his battered, scratched hands were long-fingered and well manicured, and his tattered shorts and shirt looked as if they had been of good quality. His watch looked expensive, too, she noted as she slid it off his wrist. She frowned as she saw the raw, chafed skin beneath it, then realized with puzzlement that the angry red marks were similar to those on his other wrist.

Wondering what could have caused that, she checked the back of the watch for an inscription. She was rewarded with a possible clue to the stranger's identity.

"To Ziggy," she read aloud. *"Love, Catherine."*

Cherish looked down at the tall, broad-shouldered, leanly muscled man in her bed. "Ziggy?" she repeated incredulously. With a sigh, she set the timepiece aside. "Maybe it's just a pet name," she murmured hopefully. "Something he'd never dare ask a stranger to call him."

She sat beside him on the bed and, using a pair of scissors, started to cut away the pathetic remains of his shirt. Once that was done—and he was naked except for his shorts—she soaked a clean rag in the warm water and began washing him, starting with his hands and working her way up.

Whoever he was, he was used to hard work, Cherish concluded, noting the finely developed muscles and tendons of his callused, sun-browned hands. His hard palms and his slender, capable fingers, with their faint dusting of sun-kissed hair, were so different from her own white, tapered, long-nailed hands.

The stranger's left palm rested lightly on top of hers as she washed his bruised knuckles, finding more cuts beneath the caked sand. She must have hurt him, for he gasped slightly in his sleep and stirred restlessly. The cuts had to be cleaned, however, so she gripped his hand when he tried to pull away.

His eyes opened then, long dark lashes fluttering to reveal glazed, confused eyes of an entrancing dark gray. He rolled his head slightly and looked up at her.

"Am I hurting you?" Cherish asked, hearing a nervous huskiness in her own voice.

He drew in a breath to speak, then winced. "*Something* hurts."

"You're pretty beat up," she confirmed. What if there were internal injuries? The thought hadn't occurred to her until now. She swallowed and tried to suppress her panic. "I'll help you," she promised, sickly aware of how limited her help would be if his injuries weren't merely superficial.

His eyes studied her disarrayed, wavy red hair, her wide-set green eyes, and her pale throat, then drifted slowly down. Her breasts felt suddenly tender inside the cups of her bra as his steady, heavy-lidded gaze fixed on them for a long moment before lowering to her belly and, finally, to her long thighs, left bare by the cut of her shorts.

When he finally looked into her eyes again, there was a dazed expression on his face. "Am I...in heaven?" he asked at last.

She was so astonished, she made a short hiccuping sound. "No. This is Voodoo Caye."

"Oh." He frowned and said slowly, "Cherish Love."

"Yes, that's right," she acknowledged.

"Are you a voodoo goddess?"

She shook her head and smiled. "I'm not even a priestess."

He took another breath, then closed his fingers tightly over hers as something pained him again. "I feel like hell," he admitted tightly.

"I'm not surprised. Try to go back to sleep, and I'll—"

"Hey, Doc! Granny says she's coming right away!" Luke cried, bursting into the cottage and running straight to the bedroom.

The stranger's gaze fluttered toward Luke, then widened slightly when he saw the indigo-blue cross painted on Luke's forehead. Cherish stared for a moment, too, since it hadn't been there before.

"Am I dying?" the stranger asked.

"No," Cherish said quickly. "That's just to protect him."

"From what?"

"From you," Luke said with a ten-year-old's deplorable honesty. "Granny says it wards off evil spirits."

"She hasn't even met me yet," the stranger responded irritably.

"You're tiring him, Luke," Cherish chided. "Maybe you should go stand guard at the front door."

She watched the boy leave, and when her eyes turned back to the stranger, he was already asleep again. Or unconscious. Cherish didn't know how to tell the difference. Hoping for the best, and eagerly listening for Granny Martinez's arrival, she continued caring for the man as best she could.

His fingers maintained their grasp around hers, even in his oblivious state, and his palm was growing warm, as if the chill was leaving his body at last. In answer to his silent, unconscious plea for reassurance, she held his hand between both of hers, letting him feel her warmth against his skin, human flesh against human flesh, the comforting sensation of being alive and safe.

He sighed, and his head rolled slowly to the side, exposing the vulnerable hollow below his strong jaw. Without realizing she intended to do it, Cherish reached down and smoothed his salt-crusted brown hair away from his face and off his neck. Her fingers lingered longer than was necessary, taking pleasure in the steady pulse at his throat, delighting in the contrast between the smooth skin of his neck and the hardened flesh of his palm.

Stunned by her own wayward thoughts, she grunted inarticulately, flung away the hand that clasped hers, and took a step back. She shook her head and attempted a rueful smile. She'd had no idea that her maternal instincts were so strong. For surely, she mused as she studied her guest, the subtle heat in her veins was caused by nothing more serious than a normal female desire to protect and care for someone who was injured, alone, and quite helpless. She was certainly not otherwise affected by the sight of this handsome stranger lying on her bed like some wounded hero out of legend.

Clearing her throat rather roughly, Cherish plunged the cloth back into the warm water and proceeded to briskly wash down the man's forearms, though she used the cloth delicately when cleaning the chafed skin at each wrist. They looked like rope burns, she realized, studying the raw marks more closely. Had he gotten tangled in the rigging of a sailboat?

The light sprinkling of brown hair on his arms was

crisp and springy, giving way to perfectly smooth skin on his upper arms. His biceps were round and hard, like young, ripening fruit, and Cherish inhaled sharply when she felt the unexpected, unbidden desire to lightly sink her teeth into the heavy muscle, which, even in repose, looked formidable.

She forced her mind on to other things as she continued ministering to her patient. Judging by his accent, he was American. Moreover, there was a roundness to his vowels and a slightly clipped edge to his consonants that, in only a few sentences, had convinced Cherish that he was also well educated. An East Coast university, perhaps? Or perhaps he merely wanted to sound like an Ivy League graduate and had taught himself to talk that way. Cherish had met both types of men and could never easily distinguish between them.

His chest was thickly muscled and heavy, and she realized that she wouldn't be able to wash his back without help. In any event, he stirred violently in his sleep when she attempted to wash the skin around his wound, and she pulled back, afraid of doing more damage than good. To her relief, Granny Martinez arrived at that moment.

"What have we here?" Granny asked in the singsong voice of the Garifuna, the Black Caribs who had brought with them to Central America their own language and their distinctive way of speaking English.

"Oh, Granny," Cherish groaned, extending a hand to the elderly black woman and drawing her closer to the bed. Neither gray hair, nor excess weight, nor the profusion of wrinkles in Granny's chocolate-brown skin could dim the woman's beauty. Youth had abandoned her decades ago, but the spiritual strength that made her face glow with joy and her dark eyes shine with mystery only grew stronger with the passage of time. She was wise in ways that Cherish was barely beginning to understand, and Cherish was grateful to be able to turn to her now. "He's wounded. There, on the shoulder. And he's all battered and beaten. He could have internal bleeding, don't you think? I don't know how to help him!"

"You relax now, Doc," Granny said. "Or else I will have two sick folks on my hands, instead of one."

"Can I watch?" Luke asked eagerly, having followed Granny into the little bedroom.

As always, Granny Martinez encouraged her grandson to learn, and so she permitted Luke to remain and assist her.

"We should take the man's pants off," Granny insisted. "Who knows what could be floating in those shorts?"

"But... I mean...he might not..." Cherish gestured vaguely to the man's face. Granny waited expectantly for a coherent sentence. When one failed to emerge from Cherish's mouth, the old woman laughed, pushed her aside and started struggling to pull the stranger's snug shorts off his slim hips.

Cherish looked away, foolishly pretending to be busy washing out her damp rags and wondering where this ridiculously impractical modesty had come from. Obviously the wet, dirty shorts should be removed from the man's body. She shrugged. Perhaps it was because he'd looked into her eyes and spoken to her. Now he was a person, not just an injured body. Or perhaps she was reluctant to look at anything below the man's waist, considering how hot her cheeks got when she studied him from the waist up.

"Well, nothing in this man's pants that shouldn't be there," Granny proclaimed. Then she added wickedly, "And *plenty* of what should be there!"

"Granny," Cherish chided, "he'd be embarrassed if he woke up now."

Granny shook her head. "Men like to be admired, Doc."

"*I* don't like to be admired," Luke said with a sniff.

Granny grinned. "Ten years from now, if you see a girl like the Doc, you'll want her to admire you plenty. Believe me."

Despite herself, Cherish glanced toward the bed. Her breath caught, and though she felt ashamed for ogling an unconscious man, she couldn't help herself. His thighs were long and lean, and they looked hard and capable. They were only lightly covered with hair, unlike his groin, where the hair grew dense, dark and springy. As Granny had indicated, the man did indeed possess an impressive display of masculine equipment, even in his relaxed condition. Shocked that she would stare at something so private, Cherish blinked hard and looked away quickly. Her eyes met Granny's.

"Getting warmer in here," Granny said slyly. "Maybe we shouldn't cover him up."

"Cover him." Cherish bit out the words, embarrassed.

To her relief, Granny drew a thin sheet far enough up the man's body for modesty, then examined him seriously, all trace of teasing vanished from her expression.

After what seemed like an hour, but was probably only a few minutes, Cherish asked in a strained voice, "How bad is he?"

"Well, he took a beating, like you said, but I don't think there's any internal bleeding. I'm surprised he didn't bleed to death from this wound on his shoulder. It must have started clotting as soon as he washed up on Indigo Beach.'' She reached for the bucket of warm water and squeezed out a fresh rag. ''He's got a big bump on his head, too. Nothing I can do for that. And see that ankle? He won't be walking around much for a few days. This shoulder, though, it needs cleaning right away.''

The stranger moaned in pain when Granny started to clean his wound. When the pain caused him to thrash about, he popped into bleary consciousness again. He looked at Granny, as she hovered above him, then down at his shoulder. After a moment, he said in a surprisingly reasonable tone, ''Do you absolutely have to do that?''

''Absolutely.''

He looked at her again and sighed. ''Don't tell me. I dreamed the other woman. The pinup girl. She was a fantasy, wasn't she?''

''The Doc?''

''She said her name was Cherish Love,'' he recalled dreamily. ''I must be a little delirious.''

''No, that's the Doc. She's right here.'' Granny leaned to one side so he could see Cherish. ''You're in her bed. She's going to take care of you.''

A smile touched his pain-whitened lips. ''Then this *is* heaven, after all.''

''We'll see about that,'' Granny said, dabbing at his wound. Then his thrashing grew worse, despite his efforts to control it, she instructed Cherish and Luke to hold him down. It was a relief to them all when he finally passed out again. Satisfied that the wound was clean at last, Granny sutured it with purple silk thread and tidy little stitches. For a terrible moment, Cherish felt her breakfast churning in her stomach, but her stern determination not to shame herself before Granny Martinez conquered her natural impulses.

Later that morning, she was once again alone in her cottage with the stranger, whose deep, even breathing seemed to bely Granny's warning that fever would probably come upon him by nightfall. Before leaving, Granny had chanted for a while, burned some feathers and hung an amulet at the foot of the bed. She had also left ointments and instructions and was now at home brewing various kinds of tea to ease the man's pain and drive away any infection or fever.

Now that he was clean and bandaged, the man didn't look quite so disreputable, though the dark five o'clock shadow on his face made him look roguish. Sexy, too.

Cherish frowned at the inappropriate thought. She herself would have hated him for ogling her and having lewd thoughts if their situations were reversed. Knowing that, however, didn't stop her from admiring his hairy chest, the washboard muscles of his stomach, or the hard bulge of one calf that lay exposed. She pulled the sheet over his leg and studied him for a moment longer.

She hoped he would wake up in a few hours so he could tell her who he was and what he had been doing out at sea during last night's terrible storm.

Pain and terror mingled in his mind, one feeding the other until both grew so ravenous they consumed him. The sea, the normally benevolent turquoise sea was flaying the sides of the boat and flinging him against its hull.

My God, what was he doing in the water?

Must get away, must get away.

Cold, black water, filling his lungs, slurping at his limbs, pulling him down, down. The sea would kill him, so *they* needn't bother to finish him off now.

Oh, God, bashed against her hull again. *The pain.* Oh, his head, his head, oh, the pain...

Did they know he was still here? Or had they given up looking? *Man overboard, man overboard.* No one could survive out here.

Swim away or play dead?

He mustn't let go of the bunny. And his other hand held the life preserver. It was his only chance. He mustn't let go of that, either.

Oh, the pain! In another minute, he wouldn't have to play dead. One more lungful of salt water, one more bash against the hull of the boat, one more drop of blood shed into the cold sea...

More fear. He was mindless with it now. The sea was full of predators. Storm or no storm, how long before one of them smelled his blood and closed in for the kill?

Oh, God, I'm sorry about everything I've ever done wrong, but does it have to end like this? Drowned or eaten alive or— Ow! Dammit!—smashed to pieces against the hull.

Then, with his head throbbing with pain and his shoulder hurting more than anything he'd ever experienced, he pushed the life preserver into an oncoming wave and kicked with all his might. He did it again, and again, and again, fighting unconsciousness, the burning in his lungs, and the pain in his body. When his muscles quivered and tried to give up, he forced them onward, because of all the unpleasant ways he might die tonight, he at least wasn't going to give *them* the satisfaction of killing him.

How far from shore was he? He slipped the life preserver over his head and kept kicking, clutching the bunny with all his strength.

Wave upon wave of water, blackness, the icy caress of death. His body quit at last, and not even his force of will could take him any farther. What would it be, he wondered, drowning or a shark?

No!

He must go on, he *must.* But his body could no longer respond to his violent will to survive.

No!

"It's all right."

"No!" *It's not all right, dammit!*

"Shh, it's all right. You're safe now."

"No, no, no..."

"Wake up, wake up. You're safe."

Cool hands. A soft voice, feminine and breathless.

"No!" He forced his eyes open. A long, panicked moan escaped him, shaming him as he recognized the woman. He was sweating, hot, breathing like he'd just had the greatest sex of his life. Pain seared his shoulder, roared through his head, throbbed in his ankle. God, was there any part of his body that *didn't* hurt?

"Cherish," he moaned, wanting to confirm her presence, the reality of her soft palm on his brow, the absence of that hellish nightmare.

"Yes. I..." Concern drew her brows together, made her green eyes look darker. She was so beautiful. Had he ever seen such a beautiful woman? He realized that he didn't know. "It was just a bad dream," she whispered.

"Yes." Beautiful women, he thought frantically. Other women. *Any* woman. Come on, surely he knew at least one woman, somewhere in the world.

"Are you all right?" she asked.

She wore a halo, like an angel. But she had said this wasn't heaven, hadn't she? His gaze flashed to the simple dresser behind her, and he saw a lantern glowing there. It cast a subtle golden color over her skin and made her red hair glow with jeweled highlights. He licked his lips and tried to answer her question. "All right? I . . . I don't know. Everything hurts."

"Granny Martinez says that there's no internal bleeding. And I'd take her word for it any day. I've been waiting for you to wake up so I could give you the tea she's brewed for you."

"She . . ." He blinked in growing confusion. "But didn't she say that you're the doctor?"

She smiled slightly, full lips moving moistly, making his mouth go dry. "It's the nickname they gave me when I got here. I'm a doctor of anthropology, not medicine. I'm barely competent to put on a Band-Aid."

"Oh." He discreetly studied her lush, full-breasted, narrow-waisted figure, her long, sleek legs, and her glorious red hair. He decided that her lack of medical skills was, at most, a negligible failing. "Cherish . . ."

"You should rest."

He nodded, then winced. "In a minute, Doc. Thanks for, you know, saving my life."

"You're welcome." She raised her brows inquisitively. There was an expectant silence. "What's your name?"

He swallowed. His stomach tightened as a terrible realization struck him. "I, uh . . ." His voice was hoarse as he met her gaze and admitted, "I don't know."

Two

"The fever has come," Granny told Cherish, examining her restless patient by the fading light of the westering sun.

"He cannot be very smart if he doesn't remember his own name," Luke said critically, watching Granny's every move.

"Shouldn't you be getting ready for bed?" Cherish prodded, tired of explaining temporary amnesia to Luke.

"When did he start growing flushed?" Granny asked, eyes closed, expression intent as her hands rested on the stranger's forehead.

"About three hours ago. When he couldn't remember his name, he got terribly agitated. He even tried to get out of bed. That's when the wound started bleeding again." She shrugged. "I gave him some of that tea to sedate him, and he was so weakened by his outburst that he fell back asleep right away." Seeking reassurance from the old woman, she asked, "What does it mean, Granny?"

Granny shook her head. "It could mean many things. Many things."

"I think it means he is not very smart," Luke said. "Sailing in a storm. Forgetting his name." Luke shook his head sadly.

"Enough," Cherish told him. "What should I do for him, Granny?"

"However weak his head might be, his body is healthy and strong," Granny assured her. "He only needs a little help from us to start mending." After a brief exercise of *obeah* magic to direct positive spiritual energy toward the sick man, Granny instructed Cherish to sponge down his body with cool water every half hour until the fever broke, and to make him drink a variety of nourishing liquids she had prepared for him in her own house.

"It's going to be a long night," Luke warned Cherish.

"We'll be back in the morning," Granny promised.

The heat was terrible, the nightmares were ferocious and tormenting, and the occasional confirmation that he was still alive was a dubious blessing. His shoulder seemed to be on fire, and the throbbing in his ankle only failed to seriously trouble him because the pain in his head was so much worse. Had someone hit him with a baseball bat or something?

He dreamed of the water again, cold and black, coming at him in merciless, violent waves while the wind howled, the heavens thundered, and the rain poured down so hard he lost all sense of direction. More than anything else, he feared sharks and barracudas. He knew they would be attracted to him by his scent, and when something big, smooth, and swift brushed past his struggling body, he thought his time was at hand.

"No!"

And then she was there again. The woman. Her soft flesh was as white and pink as some nymph in a Rubens painting, her eyes as green as a cat's, her breasts so round and full he longed to pillow his head on them. Her red hair brushed his cheek as she leaned over him, and he turned his face into it, inhaling its sultry fragrance, brushing his lips against a few silken strands.

She pulled the sheet back, and the cool breeze that wafted across his body made him realize that he was naked. And she was touching him, bathing his hot skin with a damp cloth, stroking the soothing coolness across his neck and shoulders, rubbing it across his ribs.

"You have the touch of an angel," he murmured, the words sounding faint and cracked. His throat ached with dryness, and his tongue felt clumsy.

She flinched and looked into his face with obvious surprise. "You're awake. You've ... you've been asleep for five hours."

He glanced at the rag in her hand. "And you've been doing this the whole time?"

"On and off."

He sighed. "I can't believe I've been missing this. Pray continue."

She hesitated, then dipped the cloth into a bucket of water, wrung it out and placed it on his chest. "What do you dream about?"

"Do you mean I'm not dreaming now?" A beautiful woman washing his naked body by candlelight, following each and every rib with long silken strokes, and she was trying to tell him this *wasn't* a dream? He gave a short, silent puff of laughter, bringing his chest into contact with her knuckles. Something tightened inside him, and he groaned.

"Does that hurt?" she asked, pausing.

"No. Not at all," he assured her, afraid she'd stop.

"Well, if you're sure it doesn't, then I think we can safely say that none of your ribs is cracked."

He watched her graceful, rhythmic movements as she turned, dipped, wrung out the cloth again and turned back to him, shaking her long, lush hair away from her face. She pressed a cool palm against his cheek to hold his head steady as she gently bathed his forehead.

"You..." She met his eyes, then looked away quickly. "You don't sleep calmly. You cry out a lot, as if your dreams are terrible." Her voice sounded a little breathless to him. Since she wouldn't meet his eyes again, he lowered his gaze. The warm mystery of her shadowed cleavage and the slight quivering of her breasts as she moved above him made his mind go numb. "What do you dream about?" she asked.

"This," he sighed.

"What?"

"Huh?" Was she wearing a bra? He couldn't tell for sure.

"I said, what do you dream about that distresses you so much?"

Pulling his thoughts together, he frowned and tried to remember. "I'm not sure. My dreams are about... drowning, death, sharks, a storm...." He scowled, trying to force the vague images into sharper focus. His head started pounding. The harder he tried to recall the dreams that Cherish said made him cry out in his sleep, the louder the pounding grew. And the pain, the throbbing pain. "Ohh..." He squeezed his eyes shut and pressed the heel of his hand against his forehead.

"Shh, it's all right. Don't think about it."

"Why can't I...?" He willed himself to calm down. Fighting for control, he drew in deep, gulping breaths, ignoring his physical pain in an effort to overcome the strange things happening to his mind. When the jungle drums stopped echoing inside his head, he slowed his breathing and started to lower his hand. Opening his eyes at that moment, he saw the angry red marks on his wrist. A quick glance at his other wrist confirmed that he had a matched set.

"What the hell is that from?" he demanded.

"You don't remember?"

"No, I..." He stared at one wrist in stupefaction. "That's not from a cheap shirt or a bad starch job. It looks like..."

"Like someone tied you up?" Cherish guessed quietly.

He drew in a sharp breath. "Rope burns?"

"Granny Martinez says they'll heal fast."

"She's the lady who was in here chanting and burning feathers earlier?"

"Yes. She's the *buye*—the shaman."

"You're putting me on."

"No."

"How does one get a job like that these days?"

Her eyes narrowed at the sarcasm in his voice. "She was chosen. I don't know all the details. That's one of the things I'm studying." At his puzzled expression, she added, "I'm an anthropologist. I'm studying the Garifuna."

He licked his lips. "I've never heard of the Garifuna."

"Most people haven't," Cherish said, her face lighting with enthusiasm as she prepared to deliver a lecture. "They're—"

"I'm sure they're fascinating," he interrupted, "but where the hell are we?"

"Voodoo Caye."

"What *country?*"

"Belize."

His eyes popped wide open and he found the strength to pick his head up off the pillow. *"Belize?"*

"Yes. You know, Belize. It's between Mexico and Guatemala. On the coast." At his blank expression, she added, "In Central America."

"I know where Belize is," he snapped, dropping his head back down to the pillow and staring at the ceiling. "But what am *I* doing here?"

"Where did you expect to be?" she growled.

"I...I don't know." He felt more confused than ever. "Belize?" He glanced at her and asked warily. "Am I...Belizean?"

"No, I think you're American."

His breath whooshed out of him with relief. "Thank God. No offense intended to the locals, Cherish, but I think I have enough problems as it is right now. I wouldn't have relished waking up to discover I'm a banana republican."

"That's hardly an appropriate..." She bit her lip and started dunking her cloth into the warm water again. "You still don't remember your name?"

His gut knotted. "No." He struggled to suppress the fear surging inside him. "Isn't that crazy?" He squeezed his eyes shut and said, more to convince himself than her, "It's on the tip of my tongue. I'll remember it in a minute."

"Do you remember anything? Your family? Where you come from? What kind of skills you have? What you were doing at sea on a night like last night?"

The pounding started in his head again, brutal and insistent. Embarrassed at the huskiness in his voice, he answered, "No. Nothing."

She got up, turned her back to him and walked over to the dresser. Her bottom looked high and round beneath her faded cutoffs, and he suddenly wondered why a woman who had so obviously been made to share pleasure with a man, was living in this spartan cottage all alone and sleeping in a bed that was barely wider than his shoulders.

She returned to the bed and held out a wristwatch to him. "You were wearing this."

He took it from her and whistled. "This thing is worth twelve, maybe thirteen thousand dollars."

"You know its value?"

"Sure." He blinked. "I was wearing this? It's mine?"

"There's an inscription," she prompted.

He turned it over and read. Then he frowned. "Ziggy?"

She nodded. "Does it sound familiar? Is that your name?"

"Ziggy?" he repeated incredulously. "Do I look like a guy who would let people call him *Ziggy?*"

"Well, until your memory returns, I think that's what we're going to have to call you."

"Ziggy," he said dully.

"What about the woman's name? Catherine. Does it make you think of anyone?"

He shook his head. "She must love me a whole lot, whoever she is. This watch is no stocking stuffer."

"If she loves you, then presumably she'll be looking for you." Cherish rose abruptly from her perch at the edge of the bed.

"Unless she died in last night's storm."

Their eyes met, their expressions troubled and confused.

"How can we find out?" he asked at last. "Can you call the American Embassy or the Coast Guard or something?"

"We don't even have a radio on Voodoo Caye," she said apologetically. "We're still having heavy winds, but as soon as the weather's better, I'll have one of the fishermen take me to Rum Point, on the mainland. I can use a phone there."

"Okay. Thanks, Cherish."

"No problem, Ziggy."

"Ziggy," he repeated without enthusiasm.

They stared at each other. He wondered if he should be feeling guilty about the instincts that assailed him as he lay in her bed, watching the shift of shadow light on her alabaster skin. Was there a woman out there somewhere, alive or dead, who had already laid claim to him? Was there a woman who would be hurt to know how much he enjoyed every sensation that tingled through his body when Cherish bathed him?

"You look tired," Cherish whispered. She placed her hand on his forehead. "You still have fever. I think you should drink more of Granny's tea, then sleep."

He suspected the tea contained substances that were either controlled or wholly illegal back home. But, he reasoned, he was hardly in any condition to point this out to his ministering angel. As he drifted off to sleep he wondered if there was, if there ever could have been, a

woman whose touch both soothed and stirred him as did
Cherish Love's?

Cherish dozed uncomfortably in a wooden chair
propped in a corner across from the bed where Ziggy
slept, tossing and turning, muttering and occasionally
making angry threats. Fear contorted his face often, and
his legs tangled violently in the thin cotton sheet that
covered his nakedness.

After a couple of hours, deep in the dead of night,
Cherish was fully awakened by a hoarse cry coming from
Ziggy's raw throat. To her dismay, he was once again
trying to get out of bed, though he didn't appear to be
fully conscious this time.

"Ziggy!" she said loudly, wondering if he would even
recognize the name. "Relax. Lie down. Get back into
bed."

He struggled to a sitting position as Cherish shot out
of her chair. Drenched with sweat and muttering incoherently, he swung his feet to the floor, then gasped in
pain when he tried to put weight on his injured ankle.

"Ziggy!" Cherish grabbed his broad, heavy shoulders
and tried to shake him. She might as well have tried to
shake a Sherman tank.

"The bunny." He panted. "The bunny."

"What bunny?" she asked frantically. A moment later
she remembered and, blinking at the absurdity of it, she
promised, "I'll bring you the bunny. Just lie down
again."

"Got to get away, get away, get away," he moaned.

"Ziggy—"

"No!" He shoved her so hard she stumbled backward
and hit the dresser with a painful thud.

"Ow! Stop it, dammit!" Growing anger and apprehension warred in her breast. Could she get him back into bed by herself, or should she risk leaving him alone for a few minutes so she could go ask Granny Martinez or one of the Martinez men to help her?

The decision was taken out of her hands. Ziggy surged to his feet, took a faltering step and got hopelessly tangled in the sheet entwining his legs. Seeing disaster ahead, Cherish reacted instinctively and lunged toward him, trying to catch him before he added to his injuries. At five-eight and one hundred forty pounds, she was no half-pint, and she was a strong woman. She had not counted, however, on Ziggy being so heavy. All that muscle felt like iron when it collided with her significantly smaller frame, and no amount of maneuvering could prevent her from sinking gracelessly to the floor with Ziggy sprawled on top of her.

"Get off! You're suffocating me," she growled.

The sudden trip seemed to have taken all the fight out of him. He lay there weakly, drawing quick, shallow breaths, his face buried in the hollow of her neck.

"Oh, God," he murmured. "Oh, God."

She didn't know if he was awake or not, but the terror in his voice was heartbreaking. What in God's name had happened to him last night? Enveloped again by that unfamiliar, vaguely fulfilling protective instinct, she wrapped her arms around him, placing one hand against the rapid rise and fall of his back while she stroked his thick, matted hair with the other. If she could just get him to calm down, perhaps he'd fall asleep again, and then she'd work out some way to haul him back into bed.

"Shh," she murmured, her fingers massaging his scalp through the salt-stiff waves of his dark hair. "It's all right. You're safe now. You're safe."

His body was so perfectly aligned with hers that her thin cotton blouse and short shorts offered no protection against the damp heat that seeped through to her skin, mingling his flesh with hers as if they were both naked, as if he were hot and sweaty from passion instead of fever.

"Oh, God, I can't make it." He sighed, his throaty voice unbearably forlorn.

She hugged him tighter, reaching out to him, into him, with some primitive instinct. "Yes, you can," she whispered fiercely, inhaling the musky scent that engulfed her, bathing in the relentless body heat that swamped her senses.

She tried to imagine the tormented images racing through his mind—the knifing, the pain, the horrifying confrontation with death in a violent, storm-tossed night.

"You're safe now. Safe," she murmured into his ear, nuzzling his hair and squeezing him tightly. She felt elemental. She was a woman feeling relieved, glad and grateful that a man had survived against the odds.

She felt his breathing change cadence, grow slower and deeper, expanding his chest rather than shaking his shoulders. He nuzzled her neck, and his unshaven jaw scraped the soft skin there. Relief, and an entirely unexpected feeling of affection, flooded her. He seemed to be surfacing now, growing calmer, more aware. His hand, which had been balled in a fist beside her head, relaxed and moved down to her waist. He squeezed it comfortingly for a moment, as if apologizing for scaring her so, then let it rest there, radiating heat, spreading his fever into her body.

"Are you all right now?" she asked. There was no answer, but he shifted his legs and his other arm so that his weight no longer rested so heavily on top of her. Though weak, he was in control again. And as his mastery of his senses strengthened, Cherish's sense of comfort evaporated.

"Ziggy?" she whispered. As the moments passed, she started to feel entirely vulnerable, trapped beneath the body of a total stranger. "Uh, Ziggy?"

"Hmm?"

When his hot mouth touched the tender spot just below her earlobe, she nearly jumped out of her skin. His lips were dry and chapped, but their effect on Cherish was more electrifying than a cattle prod. He obviously noticed their dryness, since he moistened them then with his tongue, not bothering to pull away even a fraction of an inch. That wet, velvety flicker along her sensitive skin made Cherish gasp as if she'd been goosed, made her quiver like a startled animal.

"Ziggy?" The word sounded more like two fast pants.

He blew softly into her ear. Cherish had always thought that was the corniest move ever invented. Until now. Now he created a tiny whirlwind inside her head. She could have sworn the room swirled. She could have sworn she was falling through the floor.

"D...d-don't, uh..." If she could just get enough breath, she'd tell him to stop. She was sure she would.

He nuzzled her hair and whispered something indistinct in her ear while his hand moved slowly and surely up over her rib cage until it reached a natural obstruction. While he traced agonizingly slow, wet kisses from her temple to her jaw, his knuckles brushed the underside of her breast, testing her shape, exploring the firmness of her flesh through her blouse and bra.

Cherish experienced a brief moment of near suffocation, then finally remembered to breathe again. But the quick, agitated breaths that followed this clever idea only made everything seem hotter, wilder, more out of control. When he cupped her breast in his palm and groaned with pleasure, heat pooled in her loins as if by magic, and she found herself writhing to get closer.

"Yes," he whispered. "*Yes.*" His breath was warm, sweetly scented with Granny's herbal brew, fanning across her face like an aromatic aphrodisiac.

She was lost then, lost in the smooth bunch and flow of his naked shoulders, the hungry caress of his hand, the sweet mystery of his tongue dipping into her mouth for their first kiss. Delighting in the butterfly flick of his velvety tongue against the roof of her mouth, she twisted her hips violently beneath him.

Things happened very fast then. He groaned and kissed her harder. His loins responded to all this pleasing stimulation. Cherish felt the rising fullness between them, the sudden twitch and throb of his body, and she reacted as if she'd been shot. Without remembering quite how it had happened, she found herself standing against the wall an instant later, trying to balance on quivering legs as she stared down at her naked companion in utter shock.

He lay sprawled on the floor, his lower legs still tangled in the sheet, his chest heaving, his male instincts clearly aroused, his lips slightly swollen and gleaming moistly and his expression befuddled.

Their gazes locked. Cherish opened her mouth to speak, but just blinked at him in blank silence, wondering what the hell she wanted to say. After several of the most interminable and embarrassing moments of her whole twenty-nine years, she saw comprehension slowly dawn in his expression, washing away the blatant sensuality there and replacing it with—she could have killed him for it—amusement.

He shifted slightly, then winced and rolled onto his back to take all the pressure off his wounded shoulder. Lying there naked, glowing with perspiration, his body bruised, his face unshaven, his manhood far from quiescent and his chestnut hair all tangled and tousled, he looked to Cherish like some rakish soldier of fortune awaiting his pleasure in his favorite bordello.

"Good God!" she said aloud. She should have thought of that before. She had sort of assumed he was some hapless American tourist or yachtsman who'd fallen from a pleasure boat during the storm, but she now realized that he could just as easily be one of the ruthless, deadly, fortune-seeking drifters who populated Central America more thickly than many of its native predators.

"Don't worry," he said. His smile was positively impertinent. "I knew it was you the whole time. Even before we started—"

"Under the circumstances, I hardly find that a comfort," she snapped. She noticed his shoulder had started seeping blood again. She would rather wrestle with a jaguar than tend Ziggy's wounds right now. "You're bleeding," she said coldly.

"I'll live." His casual disregard for his own health increased her suspicion that he was an unsavory character. Every man she'd ever known would whine and demand attention in Ziggy's condition. Instead, he ignored the laceration and studied her. He must be *used* to being wounded, she thought, bypassing several links in the chain of logic. Ziggy's gaze drifted down her body with a faint tinge of regret, then he sighed. "Ah, well. I suppose I'll have to get back into bed without your help?" He raised one brow inquisitively.

"I think you can get there alone."

"I think you'd let me sleep on the floor before you'd touch me again," he guessed, apparently still amused. Cherish wanted to kick him. The feeling multiplied geometrically when he said, "If it's any consolation, you're a great kisser. *Great.*"

"Please, don't—"

"No, really," he insisted, his voice glowing with awful mischief. "I don't normally get, you know, like *this* after only two or three kisses."

That statement made her straighten up so quickly she bumped into the dresser. "You remember something?" she uttered. "You remember—" Her face flushed with heat, but she doggedly continued, "You remember doing, you know..." She cleared her throat. "You remember something?"

"Hey..." He drew in a quick breath and propped himself up on his good elbow, his face alert and serious now. The intense concentration in his expression as he tried to chase down the image, the thought, the memory, showed her a new side of Ziggy. He actually looked intelligent. Much more intelligent than she would have guessed. In her experience, men were divided into two groups: intellectuals who paid scant attention to maintaining their bodies, and jocks who would rather undergo physical torture than pursue an idea. Considering how brawny Ziggy was, she was surprised at how Byronesque he looked when he concentrated.

"For a moment there," he murmured, "I had a...I don't know. There were familiar feelings. Touching a woman, making love... I felt like I'd done it before. Often, I mean. Like I had a lot of...previous experience." He glanced up, and his serious gray eyes brightened with laughter again. "What was your impression, Doc? Did I seem like I knew what I was doing?"

"Maybe your memory will start to return after you've had a little more rest." Her voice was crisp and school-marmish.

"Or we could fool around a little more. See if it stimulates my memory," he suggested.

"I think you're overstimulated as it is. Get back in bed. I'm going to go heat up some more of that tea. You're still feverish."

He sighed dramatically. "Well, if you won't help me..."

Cherish beat a hasty retreat and sought the haven of her little, primitive kitchen. She warmed up some tea while he grunted, groaned and cursed in the next room, hauling himself into bed much more theatrically than was necessary.

As Cherish watched Granny's brew return to a boil, the turmoil in her mind permitted only one pertinent thought to emerge. Who the hell was Ziggy, and what was she going to do with him?

Three

Cherish didn't sleep at all after Ziggy had drunk more of Granny's brew. He drifted back into exhausted slumber. He slept more quietly now, and Cherish guessed his fever was growing less severe, though she had no intention of touching him to find out.

She wasn't blind or naive. She had noticed the way he had looked at her during his brief moments of consciousness. What had he called her? *The pinup girl.*

It wasn't her fault that she looked the way she did, Cherish thought with frustration. She knew what men saw when they looked at her. The D-cup breasts, slender waist, curving hips, round bottom, long legs, wild red hair and green eyes, which appeared to possess all the intelligence of your average gatepost. Thanks to an utterly random and unfair assemblage of chromosomes, Cherish had been hounded, pursued, pestered and literally slavered over by men since she was fourteen years old. And it really made her dislike the whole gender.

Life is all about love, her ultraromantic mother always said. *Find a man who truly loves you, and all your burdens will seem light, Cherish.*

But Mom had never told Cherish how she was supposed to be able to recognize a true devotion of the heart when every boy she met could think of nothing but pulling her down in the backseat of his car.

When the right one comes along, you'll know, her father had said.

"How, Dad?" she had finally asked in exasperation. At nineteen, she was starting to despair of experiencing anything more tender than lustful gazes and heavy-handed passes. "When a guy won't take his eyes off my, uh, chest the whole time we're out, how am I supposed to look into his eyes and know if he's the right one?"

Well, it was the wrong question to ask a father. She was usually very careful not to mention her experiences with the opposite sex to her father, because she really didn't want him to spend the rest of his life in jail for the murder of half the boys at her university.

"Your father looked that way at me when we were young," Mom said, when a twenty-one-year-old Cherish had complained about the way every single male she encountered stared heatedly at her.

"And you *married* him?"

"It was so romantic!"

"But, Mom, they *all* look at me like that!" She had stopped telling her mother about the groping and grabbing, too, since she felt she was too old now to be continually enveloped in her mother's comforting, protective embrace. Besides, the woman who had named her daughter Cherish Dear Love—Cherish groaned every time she thought of her full name—would have probably believed all that pawing was motivated by romantic sentiments instead of overbearing hormones.

Ultimately academia had been the solution to Cherish's lifelong problem. It was her refuge, to some extent. Men were men, whatever their vocation, but some men were so intellectual, so divorced from their senses, that their reaction to Cherish's appearance was often minimized to a bearable degree. Of course, she frequently had to overcome reverse discrimination. The first day she walked into a new professor's class while working on her master's degree, he had mistaken her for a cheerleader and directed her to the gymnasium. She also knew—because the more secret a piece of gossip is, the faster it boomerangs back to the person least meant to hear it— that she had been denied a grant she deserved because, after the interview, it had been deemed evident that no woman who looked like Cherish could possibly be a serious anthropologist.

Other memories, bitter, angry recollections of the teaching position at Barrington College, the position that should have been *hers,* washed over her. She stalked around her humble kitchen on Voodoo Caye, banging pots and pans and pumping water with vigor.

How glad she was to be here, she thought, feeling renewed gratitude toward her supervisor, Grimly Corridor, who ran the Institute in Belize City. He was an eccentric old slave driver who had never treated her like anything except an ordinary young anthropologist. Grimly was obstreperous, obsessed, unreasonably demanding and unpardonably rude, but he had never ogled Cherish, made a pass, or implied that she was too pretty to be smart.

Of course, she wasn't without normal human drives.
Besides, her mother was always harping about how glorious love was.

"I even married a man named Love, Cherish," Mom
often said. "Reach out and touch someone."

"Yes, Mom. Pass the potatoes, would you?"

Consequently Cherish had taken a lover during the final year of her master's program. She had chosen him
very carefully. He was a shy, distracted archaeological
student who never got excited about a woman unless she
was considerably older. Older as in a mummified woman
from the Egyptian New Kingdom of some two thousand
years ago.

Cherish's chosen lover was safe. He was thoughtful.
And if he was a little dull, if she had forgotten almost
everything about him within a month after their breakup,
at least he had never made Cherish feel like a sex object,
a hunted animal, *a . . . a pinup girl.* He would never have
dragged her down on the floor after less than one day's
acquaintance, lain naked on top of her and started kiss-
ing her. And he never would have grinned remorselessly
at such appalling behavior.

She was going to have to show Ziggy who was boss,
Cherish concluded. Okay, so he had gotten away with
something that no one else ever had; a total stranger, he'd
made her cling to him like Velcro. But it was nothing to
worry about. Her guard had been down, she'd been tired
and he had . . . employed certain skills she had never encountered before, but there was definitely no question of
its happening again. And if he thought that there was,
well, she had nearly fifteen years of experience at deal-
ing with men who thought they could have their way with
her. She could handle one wounded amnesia victim.

The mental reminder of Ziggy's memory loss turned Cherish's thoughts in a new direction. Who was he? Why couldn't he remember anything? Who was Catherine? What was the *Lusty Wench?*

What were they going to do if he didn't start remembering who he was and where he belonged?

"Where's my bunny?"

Cherish jumped, dropped the pot she'd been holding and whirled to face her patient, who was standing in the doorway of the bedroom. The bedsheet was held modestly, though precariously, around his waist, and he was leaning against the doorframe so he wouldn't have to put weight on his bad ankle. Seeing him standing for the first time, she became fully aware of just how powerful a man he was. Not just his body, which was a work of tall, lean, beautifully sculpted muscle and bone, despite the bruises and scratches; his presence, his posture, his very manner all bespoke a man who was confident and assured of getting whatever he wanted.

"You're awake," Cherish said inanely.

"The way you've been banging those pots around, the whole island is probably awake by now," he responded.

"I see we're a trifle irritable today."

"Where's my bunny?"

"Your bunny?"

"My bunny. My bunny," he repeated with growing impatience. "I know I had it with me when you found me on the beach. Where is it?"

"I . . ." She tried to remember where she had deposited the loathsome thing.

His face blanched. "You didn't throw it away?" he rasped.

"No, it's . . . oh! I know!" Cherish went to retrieve it from the pile of newspapers upon which she had laid it yesterday. Again holding it gingerly by its ear, she said, "It's still rather soggy."

"Give me that. I can't believe you took my bunny away."

"Calm down," she chided. "Really, a man of your age carrying on about a stuffed animal."

"You don't know my age," he reminded her, taking the bunny and regarding it with some disfavor.

"Thirty? Thirty-two?"

He shrugged. "If I remember, I'll tell you."

"Still no memory at all?"

"I remember last night pretty well."

Their gazes locked. Cherish felt herself tumbling into the smoky depths of his gray eyes. With a visible tremor, she broke off the contact and said, "What's with the bunny, Ziggy? It's hideous."

He frowned at it. "Yeah, it is, isn't it?"

About eighteen inches in length, the bunny was fat, with stubby limbs and overlong ears. It was a revolting pink, though the color looked considerably faded after its long drenching in the Caribbean. Its face was white, with an awful, stiff grin painted for a mouth and cheap two-tone buttons for its eyes; one eye was missing, though.

"Made in Guatemala," Cherish murmured, reading the pink-stained label that hung off one drooping ear. "You nearly died two nights ago. Hanging on to this thing while swimming through a raging storm could have made the difference between life and death, Ziggy. Why did you keep it?"

"I'll be damned if I know." The sheet he held around his waist slipped slowly to his hips as he studied the bunny. Cherish's gaze dropped briefly to his hard abdomen, his navel, the light trickle of downy brown hair that disappeared into the barrier of the sheet, the faint indentation where his thigh and torso joined.... "What?" he asked suddenly.

"Huh?"

"You made a noise like...I don't know. A noise."

"Maybe you should sit down," she suggested. "Get off that ankle."

"Help me to the table?" He batted his lashes at her. Cherish eyed him suspiciously. "Strictly a charitable business. I promise."

"Okay," she agreed with ill-concealed reluctance. "Here."

He slipped his right arm over her shoulders. She wrapped her arm around his bare waist and felt the heat of his smooth skin under her fingers, felt the subtle shift of muscle under her palm. He smelled far too good for a man who'd been drenched in nothing but salt water and sweat for the past two days. He felt too good for a man who had treated her like a common sex object last night. He was just the right height, she thought, then wondered, the right height for what?

He lowered himself into one of the rickety chairs at her stained little kitchen table and settled cautiously into a sitting position. "Don't you have any comfortable furniture in this house?" he demanded. "A bed of nails would be preferable to that bed, and all your chairs look like they belong in some New York rehearsal hall. The kind of place where cadaverous, unemployed actors sit around being intense."

"You've been to New York?" Cherish asked quickly, taking the seat opposite him.

"I... Yes!" He looked at her with delight, his gray eyes alert, his dark brows raised. "Yeah, I know New York well."

"Do you live there?"

He shook his head. "I don't know, Cherish. I can see the streets in my mind. I know all the landmarks—the Empire State Building, the U.N., the World Trade Center, Lincoln Center, Times Square, the Plaza Hotel.... There's a store downtown that sells nothing but condoms."

Cherish blinked. "Can you remember anything personal? Places you've stayed, eaten, shopped? Besides the condom store, I mean. Can you think of anyone who knows you there? Catherine, for example?"

He frowned, and she could see his jaw working. After a moment he made a stifled sound of pain and pressed a fist to his temple. "Why does it hurt like this when I start trying to remember who I am?"

"Shh," Cherish soothed. "It's all right. I've read about this. I think it's called psychogenic amnesia."

"I wish you hadn't said *amnesia*. It sounds so serious."

"It's not so much a memory *loss* as a memory, uh, cover-up. The forgotten material is still in your head, beneath the level of consciousness. You'll be able to access it eventually."

"Why can't I access it now?"

"This isn't my field," she said modestly.

"Cherish." His voice was impatient.

"Well, as I understand it—and, at best, I understand it in a very shallow and superficial sense—"

"*Cherish.*"

"You're probably suffering from a dissociative disorder."

"What happened to my amnesia?"

"Amnesia *is* a dissociative disorder. The victim—"

"Do you have to use the word *victim?*"

"The, uh, amnesiac undergoes an experience so severe and traumatic that he must dissociate himself from it in order to... keep on going. The event could be a natural disaster, physical injury or the threat of physical injury, death or a close call with death, terrible tragedy, and so on."

Ziggy glanced down at his wounded shoulder, which needed cleaning again. "I appear to have been through several of those things," he remarked.

"So your mind blotted out whatever happened to you. Stabbing, near drowning, the storm... Who knows what else? That information is still there. Hence, your nightmares. The problem is, in suppressing the horror of that night, you've suppressed all other personal information about yourself."

He was quiet for a long moment before he asked, with a casualness that didn't deceive Cherish at all, "So, how long does this last, Doc?"

"Well, it's possible that you may subconsciously choose never to remember the events of that night."

"What about the rest of my life?" he demanded.

"I don't know, Ziggy," she admitted. "I believe that memory eventually returns in most cases. It would undoubtedly help if you were in familiar surroundings, with familiar people. Unfortunately you washed up with no ID. I'll go over to the mainland today to use a phone and learn what I can. Hey! What does the *Lusty Wench* mean to you?"

"Lusty wench?" His expression changed. "Dare I say it makes me think of you at about three o'clock this morning?"

She scowled at him. "According to your life preserver, you fell off the *Lusty Wench*. If we can trace the boat, we may be able to find out who you are."

"That's an encouraging thought."

"And your memory could return at any moment, too," she added encouragingly.

"But why do I know so many other things?" he wondered aloud. "I can name every state in the United States, and most of their capitals. I know some Shakespeare by heart—I tried it before I got out of bed this morning. I know that penicillin comes from mold, the Berlin Wall fell and George Bush didn't get reelected. How can I know these things, but not know my own name? Why can't I remember who I am, or what the *Lusty Wench* is, or who Catherine is?"

His frustration pierced her heart and made her long to help him. He was so clearly a man who was unused to being helpless. "What about the bunny? What connects you to it?" God forbid, she thought with fear, that it had belonged to a child who might have been lost in that storm.

"I don't know," he answered, turning the stuffed animal over and over in his hands. "I woke up thinking about it, thinking I had to know where it was, have it with me, keep it safe. Now why would I care about keeping this damn thing safe?"

She didn't know why her throat hurt when she asked, "Could it belong to someone important to you?"

"Cherish, I would never give something this ugly to someone important to me. I know what you're thinking. But if I've got a kid somewhere, then I'm sure I buy its toys at FAO Schwartz."

"Maybe you can't afford FAO Schwartz."

"Then life would hardly be worth living, and I wouldn't have struggled so hard to survive the other night. No, Cherish, whoever I am, I'm sure I'm rich."

She choked on laughter which she thought might not be appropriate. "If you say so, Ziggy."

"I was wearing a twelve-thousand-dollar watch," he reminded her.

"Which you can't be sure is yours."

He looked thoughtful. "Are you saying I might have stolen it?"

The question made her uneasy, and she tried to avoid answering it. "I should go see if someone can take me to Rum Point this morning."

"You didn't answer my question."

"And you should shower and shave," she added, getting up.

He grabbed her arm when she would have walked past him and hauled her to his side with surprising strength for someone who was injured and ill. "Well?"

His expressive eyes had turned cool and steely, and the angry scratch running down the right side of his face, as well as the bruise around his left eye, made him look piratical and dangerous. Cherish felt her breasts rise and fall in agitation, scraping along the inside of her clothes until the nipples felt tender.

"I don't know what to think," she whispered. "You could be a wealthy, upstanding American who was attacked by drug runners or Gulf pirates. Or..." She shrugged. "I don't know, really."

"But you're wondering what kind of man washes ashore with a knife wound and no identification," he guessed.

"There was nothing in your shorts."

They stared at each other for a long, tense moment. His grip on her arm softened, grew caressing. His palm was warm, hard, firm. Cherish became intensely aware of the sheet that sagged between his legs, barely covering his groin, leaving his hips and abdomen bare. He radiated energy, heat, and a raw, immodest sexuality that overwhelmed her as he reached out carefully with his injured arm and took her hand in his.

With another of those sudden, unsettling changes of expression, his eyes sparkled with laughter and he said, "*Nothing* in my shorts? I could prove you wrong, if you're interested, Doc."

She felt paralyzed by the sultry heat in his gaze, by the subtle, unspoken promise of his touch. Struggling for air, she whispered, "How can you think about...about sex right now?"

He shrugged with one shoulder and leaned toward her, lifting his face up to her, moistening his lips for a kiss as his good arm slid around her waist. "Maybe I'm always like this. But, to tell the truth, I've got a strong intuition that you bring it out in me, Doc."

She gasped and stepped hastily away, making him grit his teeth as a dozen different muscles protested his involuntary effort to pursue her. Backing away, Cherish scowled at him, feeling offended and hurt—and more tempted than she was willing to acknowledge.

"I don't *want* to bring it out in you."

"I can tell," he conceded, settling back in his chair. His gaze raked over her simple ponytail, her utilitarian khaki shirt and shorts, and her sensible shoes. "But you've got a quality, Dr. Love, that makes me forget I'm supposed to be weak and injured." He cocked his head and added, "And you've got a way of staring back that makes me think you sometimes forget about it, too."

She was saved from having to think of a reasonable, mature response to that remark, because Granny and Luke Martinez arrived at that moment, bustling into the open doorway of the cabin with a flurry of energy and a heavy burden of food.

"Granny made you some porridge," Luke announced. He added quietly to Ziggy, "You don't want to eat the Doc's cooking."

"It's good to see you wide-awake." Granny beamed at her patient. "How do you feel this morning?"

"A lot better," Ziggy admitted. "I imagine that has a lot to do with you, Granny."

She nodded and added, "This is my grandson, Luke."

"Do you remember your name, yet?" Luke asked.

"We think it's Ziggy," Ziggy answered.

"Ah!" Luke looked pleased, as if the stranger might not be quite as hopelessly stupid as he had initially feared. "That is a good name."

"Well, it'll do," Ziggy said with less enthusiasm.

"Do you remember anything else?" Granny asked.

"No." He glanced at Luke. "Is that why the kid still has a blue cross painted on his forehead? You think evil spirits took away my memory?"

"Perhaps," Granny said, unpacking the food. "Or perhaps you came face-to-face with them, and they were so horrible, you have thrown your memory into the sea."

"I can't stay for breakfast, Granny," Cherish said. "I've got to find someone to take me to Rum Point so I can phone Dr. Corridor's office and the American Embassy in Belize City."

"Ziggy won't be able to travel for a while," Granny advised her.

Maybe so, but Cherish was determined to get rid of him at the first possible opportunity. And from the look in his eyes, he knew it. She avoided meeting his gaze again as she collected various items she needed for this trip and left her cabin with a clipped farewell.

Ziggy was starved, and he literally didn't know when he had last eaten. He dug into Granny's cooking, washing it down with fresh juice and strong coffee, and chatted with the small black child who stared at him with open fascination.

With a skill that felt strangely familiar, Ziggy ensured that they kept returning to the topic that interested him the most.

"The Doc? She's been here about six months," Luke told Ziggy. "She's supposed to stay for at least two years."

"Does she have a boyfriend?"

Luke's face wrinkled at the distasteful subject. "No. She's a serious girl. No men except for that Dr. Corridor she writes and calls, and he's her boss."

"Let me look at those stitches," Granny said.

It was while she was examining her handiwork that Ziggy noticed the purple thread she had used. "A new fashion statement in sutures, Granny," he teased.

"Tell the Doc to clean it again before you go to bed tonight," Granny advised. She smiled absently and added, "She needs a man in her life."

"Why are you so interested in the Doc?" Luke asked.

"I haven't got much else to think about. I can't remember anything else."

"Luke will stay with you today, since Cherish will be gone a long time," Granny said. "He'll wash the bedclothes and hang them out to dry, so they'll be nice and clean when you go back to bed."

"I'd like to merit clean sheets," Ziggy remarked. "The Doc said something about a shower?"

"It's behind the house," Luke said. "I'll help you."

"Kid, I can't say for sure, but I'll bet I've been showering for years without help."

"Ah, but this is not like mainland plumbing," Luke warned. "I'll show you how to use it."

"And then I'm going to go through that stack of newspapers," Ziggy decided, looking at the pile Cherish had stacked neatly near the door. "Maybe something there will jog my memory."

But he had an uneasy feeling that the clues to the only things he really needed to know were not in any newspaper, but buried deep in his own subconscious.

Four

It was after dark when Cherish finally returned from the mainland, feeling confused, wary and more than a little irritable. Given Ziggy's condition when she had left, Cherish expected to find him resting quietly. Indeed, she hoped he was sound asleep so she wouldn't have to face him before morning. She had no idea what to make of the scant information her phone calls had uncovered today.

Consequently, she was not only surprised to find her modest little cabin blazing with gas lanterns as she approached it, she was also downright annoyed to hear a chorus of rowdy masculine laughter coming from within. When she flung open the door and stumbled inside, tripping over Peter Sacqui's three-legged dog, she came face-to-face with half the male population of Voodoo Caye.

"It's the Doc!" Luke cried cheerfully, as if she were a long-awaited guest.

"Hey, Doc! Come on in," called Peter Sacqui, a handsome, young, easygoing fisherman. Cherish knew that all the unmarried girls on Voodoo Caye had their eyes on him.

Peter's suggestion was followed by half a dozen other friendly invitations for Cherish to enter her own home and join the party. The air was thick with smoke since, like everyone else in Belize, many Garifuna smoked too much. Cherish inhaled, prior to demanding what was going on, and promptly started choking on the thick fumes.

Daniel Nicholas, a respected, middle-aged member of the community, stepped forward, pushed Peter's dog out of Cherish's way and patted Cherish on the back. After a few unpleasant moments, during which Cherish's gurgles and sputters were the focus of everyone's attention, Daniel asked, "Okay, Doc?"

She wiped her eyes and nodded. A few cautious breaths assured Cherish she could inhale safely, as long as she didn't do it too deeply. Those shallow breaths also made her realize something else. Daniel Nicholas smelled of rum, and so did everyone else around her.

"What's going on here?" she demanded.

"Now, come on, fellas. Where are your manners?" Ziggy chided. Recognizing his voice, Cherish scanned the room. "The Doc's had a long, hard day, and now's she developing a hacking cough. Find her a seat, guys."

When half a dozen men immediately shot out of their chairs and offered them to Cherish, she finally spotted Ziggy. Wearing nothing but a pair of *her* shorts, which he had borrowed without permission, and which he had undoubtedly obtained by raiding *her* dresser, he was reclining in a hammock, which had inexplicably materialized in her kitchen since that morning. The ropes supporting it disappeared through opposing open windows and were evidently attached to trees outside the cabin. The hammock's position put Ziggy within convenient reach of the kitchen table, which was covered with playing cards, money and dirty glasses.

"Where did that hammock come from?" Cherish asked in confusion.

"My old fishing nets," Daniel Nicholas explained, gesturing with his dark, work-roughened hands.

"But what's it doing in my kitchen? Right in my way!"

"Ziggy's ankle hurt and his fever made him dizzy. He had to lie down," Luke explained with great exuberance. Cherish wondered suspiciously if the boy had been drinking rum, too.

"There's a perfectly good bed in the next room," Cherish said, looking directly into Ziggy's blandly innocent eyes. He rolled them. She resisted the urge to maim him—not because he didn't deserve it, but because the room was full of witnesses.

"Ziggy don't like that bed, Doc," Peter said. "You shouldn't make him sleep there."

"*Make* him sleep there?" She whirled on Peter. "He was practically dead when I found him on Indigo Beach yesterday morning! I gave him my own bed! *I've* been sleeping in a wooden chair since he got here."

Peter grinned good-naturedly. "Then aren't you glad we put up this hammock for him? He can still reach the card table, and you can have your bed back. See? Everything works out for the best."

Cherish put a hand to her brow, feeling slightly dizzy herself. "Card table? That's my kitchen table. What's going on here?"

"Ziggy read all your old newspapers," Luke explained. "He showered, he napped, he had some broth for his lunch and he napped again. Then he got bored. You can't blame him.''

Ziggy attempted to look blameless. Before Cherish could tell him that it was a failed effort, Daniel Nicholas took up the narrative. "So when we were done with the day's work,'' he said, "Ziggy invited us all over. Showed us how to play some new poker games.''

"Gambling?'' Cherish bleated. "You were *gambling?*''

"Now, Doc,'' Ziggy said, lounging in his hammock, "I think you're taking an unnecessarily dim view of a friendly little game of cards.''

"How much have you won?'' she asked him.

"Come on, Cherish—''

"How much?'' she repeated stonily.

"I'm not sure,'' he admitted. "It's all Belizean money.''

She pushed through the crowd of men, none of whom had yet resumed their seats, and looked down at the pile of money, which lay on the table in front of Ziggy. "That looks like about fifty dollars Belizean.''

"Is that a lot?'' he asked.

"Give it back,'' she ordered.

Ziggy sighed, shrugged and reached for the money. The rest of the men, however, protested loudly. What was the matter with her? they demanded. Did she honestly think a good man like Ziggy had been cheating them? Did she think they needed *her* to protect them? Did she think they couldn't eventually win their money back, fair and square? Did she think Ziggy was the only good player among them?

"Doc, *I* won sixty dollars,'' Peter insisted.

"And Ziggy gave me five dollars for keeping the bugs away," Luke added eagerly. "And he lets me see all his cards and how he bets, so I can learn to play, too."

"That's enough!" Cherish said, holding up her hands in a gesture that silenced them all. Having no idea what to do about this development, but decidedly uneasy about its ramifications, she decided that the best temporary measure would be to get them all out of the cabin so she could talk to Ziggy alone. "Look, I'm sorry to break up the party, but Ziggy's right. I've had a long, hard day, and I'd really like to go to bed now."

"Sure. Good night, Doc," said Peter, resuming his seat. Everyone else followed suit. Cherish sighed heavily.

"Uh, lads, I believe what Dr. Love means is she'd like you all to go home now," Ziggy said.

"Oh!" Peter rose again, smiling sheepishly, and began pocketing his winnings. "Sorry, Doc." He murmured to Dog-Dog, his three-legged companion, and left with a vague wave.

Cherish smiled politely and nodded good-night to each departing man. "Time for you to go, too," she said severely to Luke, who stalled behind the others.

"But Granny said to make sure Ziggy eats his supper. That's why I came over here. I brought some *wowla* in broth."

Cherish wrinkled her nose. "I'll see that he eats it. Thank Granny for me."

"And his stitches need cleaning."

"I'll take care of it. Good night, Luke."

"And he needs a shave. You can see he needs a shave."

"Yes, Luke. Good night, Luke. I'll shave him, I promise." She urged Luke out the door, closed it firmly behind him, then turned back to Ziggy. They eyed each other for a long, tense moment.

Ziggy was the first to break the silence. He ran a hand over his beard-roughened jaw and said, "Dare I let you near me with a razor, Dr. Love?"

"Not if you value your life."

"I sense you're a trifle upset about something."

Cherish unleashed her temper. "How *could* you?"

"How could I what?"

His wide-eyed show of innocence infuriated her. "How could you contaminate a traditional culture?"

"Excuse me?"

"Grimly is going to be furious when he finds out."

"Grimly?"

"My boss, Grimly Corridor."

"*Grimly?*" he repeated, clearly diverted.

She nodded impatiently. "Who knows how this might affect my study of the community?"

"Oh, come on, Cherish. How naive can you be? Do you seriously imagine that none of those men has ever played poker before? Peter didn't win sixty dollars through sheer dumb luck." He grinned mischievously and added, "However, none of them had played Montana Red until I showed them how."

"It's not funny!"

"Come on, Doc, even a serious anthropologist surely can't see any harm in a friendly little game of chance," he said in a wheedling way.

Cherish snapped her mouth shut on her next retort and tried to organize her thoughts. She was permitting tonight's events to sidetrack her from what they most needed to discuss. Deciding it would be best to get a grip on her temper before she broached the subject uppermost in her mind, she went to the stove, where Granny's broth was simmering, and asked over her shoulder, "Have you started remembering things?"

"Nothing useful." He sounded suddenly demoralized. "But when I picked up that deck of cards... Look."

She turned around. He slid out of the hammock, favoring his damaged shoulder and ankle, sat at the table and gathered together all the cards. Then his slim, long-fingered hands cut, shuffled and spread them out with all the flourish of a magician or a casino dealer. With a deft flick, he turned the entire row of cards over, from face-down to faceup, as easily as if he'd been doing it all his life.

Cherish felt her stomach clench involuntarily. Somehow, this seemed to fit in with what she had learned today. Watching his obvious expertise, she asked through stiff lips, "Did you cheat tonight?"

He didn't even show offense at her question; he was too busy frowning down at his hands as they continued to expertly maneuver the cards. "No. I didn't need to. I don't know how I learned it, but I'm a pretty good poker player. I even purposely lost a few hands. What would I spend the money on around here, anyhow? Besides, Cherish," he said, looking up at last, "I'm not going to steal money from a bunch of hardworking fishermen who've been nice to me. I'd have to be a real skunk to do that, wouldn't I?"

"But do you..." She felt embarrassed, but persisted, "Are you some kind of card shark?"

He shrugged, and a distant, pensive expression spread across his face, making his Byronic features look dreamy and whimsical. "I don't think so, but who the hell knows? I... can see a casino.... The croupier's speaking French: *Mesdames et messieurs, faites vos jeux! Les jeux sont faits. . . .''* He closed his eyes, trying to remember.

"Where are you?" Cherish whispered, hoping this memory might suggest something conclusive about her mysterious guest.

Ziggy shook his head slightly. He dropped the deck of cards and brought both hands up, tangling them in the gleaming waves of his thick, chestnut hair. It looked soft and healthy now that he'd had a chance to wash it. The long muscles of his forearms stood out when he balled his hands into fists and pressed them against his forehead.

"Someplace elegant," he whispered, his voice coming from deep in his throat as he concentrated. "Foreign. All the waiters are speaking French. So are the women."

"Do you speak it, too?" she asked.

"Français? Oui, je le parle assez bien." Ziggy raised his head suddenly, blinking his eyes rapidly. "My God, I speak French! Where did I learn that?"

"Any other languages? Spanish, maybe?"

"I don't know. Say something in Spanish."

"¿Tienes hombre?"

He looked at her blankly.

"I asked if you were hungry," she said.

"Oh. No, I guess I don't know any Spanish. Just French, and enough German and Italian to pick up pretty girls." He blinked again and looked at her. "I don't know where *that* came from."

"Maybe it's a favorite saying of yours." She couldn't help smiling. "Do you know *how* you learned enough French to gamble and enough German and Italian to pester women?"

He frowned, trying to remember. The dark stubble on his cheeks and jaw was highlighted by the flicker of the lanterns, making him appear dark and dangerous. But when he looked off into the distance again, his gray eyes filled with frustration and uncertainty, he suddenly seemed so forlorn, lost and alone in the strange, blank world he'd been born to only yesterday. Cherish, who only moments ago had been ready to strangle Ziggy, now felt an unwelcome flood of sympathy for him as he struggled to remember something—anything—more from his past.

Cherish's anger diminished, slipping away like a wave receding from the sandy shore. She realized that, after an entire morning and afternoon with only ten-year-old Luke Martinez for company, the gaping void in Ziggy's memory may have become too heavy to bear alone. The sudden need to escape from the echoing emptiness of the past was probably what influenced him to host that impromptu poker game in Cherish's home. His irreverent comments and overactive libido provoked her so much, it was easy to forget how afraid he must be. She rather suspected he wanted her to forget; a man like Ziggy probably didn't relish the knowledge that Cherish had recently had a front-row seat in the theater of his nightmares.

To her surprise, her ire continued to fade as she began cleaning the kitchen, which was littered with evidence of Ziggy's recent debauchery. The room still smelled of smoke, so she maneuvered around the hammock to fan the fumes toward the windows, thankful that Ziggy himself was a nonsmoker—or had perhaps forgotten that he smoked. She piled dirty cups and glasses into the sink and took Ziggy's glass of rum away from him when he reached for it, after admitting that he couldn't recall anything else just now.

"Hey!" he protested, reaching out for the glass as she whisked it away. He groaned and winced as his wounded shoulder and aching muscles protested at this sudden movement.

"A man in your condition shouldn't be drinking," Cherish said sternly, quite unaffected by the scowl he cast at her.

"How would you know, Dr. Love?"

"Granny prescribed broth, not rum. Here, eat this." She ladled some broth and boiled *wowla* into a bowl and placed it before him.

"I'm not hungry." He grumbled. "Only two things would make me feel better right now, and you've already said I can't have either one."

"No rum, Ziggy." His other chosen pastime struck her as inadvisable for a variety of reasons. "As for the poker—"

"Actually I wasn't referring to poker. I just did that to keep busy."

"Then what else would make you feel better?"

His gaze met hers meaningfully, and the sudden heat between them made her belly curl with unwanted desire. She had never before believed a man could make a woman's pulse race just by looking at her, but now Cherish's heartbeat picked up speed, drumming inside her chest, echoing in her ears. Ziggy's gray eyes grew cloudy and opaque, full of secret knowledge and veiled promise, and his dark brows lowered speculatively as a slight smile curved his full lips. Cherish backed up a few steps, breathing shallowly, suddenly thankful that Ziggy's injured ankle prevented him from pursuing her across the room.

"No, uh..." Her voice lodged in her throat. She swallowed, transfixed by his gaze, and tried again. "No more, um..."

"No fooling around?" he supplied helpfully.

She nodded. "Uh-huh. We agreed."

"I don't remember agreeing." His voice was husky, distracted.

"You're a guest in my house. An *uninvited* guest," she observed.

"Cherish."

His voice caressed her name. His lips parted as he extended a hand to her, openly challenging her with his silent invitation to come closer. She didn't and he sighed, relaxing back into his seat after a tense moment. "All alone here today, with only a child for company, and no memories to look back on, I thought about you, Cherish. Why is this beautiful young woman living in the middle of nowhere like this? Why does a woman who kisses like she's starving, sleep alone on a bed of nails?"

She flushed with humiliation, because she *had* felt like she was starving when she'd kissed him. "You have no idea what my habits—"

"I asked. In a village like this, everyone knows everything. Six months here, and you still haven't got a lover." He looked at her curiously. "Why, Cherish? Plenty of men on Voodoo Caye find you attractive, and I doubt prejudice is one of your flaws."

She was shocked. "The Garifuna on Voodoo Caye are my study group! I can't interact sexually with them! My findings would be questionable and my scholarly reputation would be irreparably—"

"And you don't write to a lover in the States," Ziggy continued. "A guy back home would wait for a woman like you, but there's no one. I don't get it, Cherish. What's your story?"

"I can't believe you're asking such personal questions!"

"Humor me," he coaxed. "I'm wounded."

"I should have thrown you back to the fish."

"Why are you living like a nun?" he persisted.

"Who's Catherine?" she demanded.

Ziggy stiffened slightly, then smiled ruefully. "Touché."

"Eat your soup."

He tasted it. "Not bad. Granny's a pretty good cook."

Cherish nodded. "She's good at a lot of things. All the food she's giving you has medicinal and spiritual qualities to help you heal." She started cleaning up the room, avoiding his eyes.

Ziggy swallowed another mouthful. "Chicken soup. The international cure-all."

"That's not chicken," Cherish said casually.

He chewed on the white meat. "Sure tastes like chicken."

"You like it?"

"Uh-huh. What is it?"

"*Wowla.*" She dumped some more dirty glasses into the sink.

"Local bird?"

"No." She fanned some of the smoke out the door, starting to enjoy herself.

"Well, what is it?"

"Boa constrictor."

He coughed so long and hard she wound up thumping him sharply on the back. "I'm eating a *snake?*"

"A cold-blooded creature . . . to help your fever," she explained with saccharine innocence.

"You should have warned me," he growled, pushing away the rest of his soup.

"You shouldn't have asked people questions about my private life," she replied.

He glared at her for a moment, then sighed and sagged in his chair. "Could we call a truce for the rest of the night? I'm feeling a little dragged out."

"No wonder. You should try to act more like a sick person," she chided.

"I can't remember how." He sounded weary.

"You don't have to eat the rest of the *wowla*, but I think you should finish the broth."

"No way. It was made with the snake."

"Ziggy—"

"I would rather drink sewer water." He shuddered. "I *hate* snakes."

"How do you know? I mean, do you remember that, or did you just decide now?"

He shrugged. "I just know. The same way I know I hate opera, politics and taxes. The way I know I like cashmere sweaters, sports cars, reggae music, Chinese food and basketball."

"All the good things in life," she said dryly.

"Please take this muck away." He was starting to look a little green.

"As you wish, sir."

"Wait!" He put his hand over hers, stopping her when she would have removed the bowl of broth. "Something's familiar."

"What?"

He frowned. "I don't know. Something about you removing my bowl. A restaurant!"

"What's it called?"

"I don't know. There's white linen, good silver..." His hand tightened on her arm. "There's someone with me," he said slowly, still staring at his broth.

"Man or woman?"

After a moment, he said, "A woman."

"What does she look like?"

"Diamonds. Discreet, not gaudy. Very expensive. First water."

"Can you see her face?"

He shook his head. "No, I—"

"Is it Catherine?"

"She's..." After a pause he let out his breath and released her arm to rub his forehead. "It's gone."

"A fancy restaurant, a woman in diamonds..." Cherish removed the broth before saying, "Ziggy, are you sure about this?"

"No, of course I'm not sure." He sounded irritable. "How could I be sure? I don't even know my own name."

"I just mean that these flashes of memory...well, they sound more like fantasies than memories. Elegant places, beautiful women, French waiters." Cherish gestured vaguely. "It's not that those *couldn't* be true memories, but there's a possibility that—"

"Would you be happier if I started having flashbacks to a cold-water tenement and food stamps?"

"No, I just mean that it's going to be hard enough as it is for you to recall your life, since there are no familiar reminders here. Everyone fantasizes about riches and a glamorous life-style. I just don't want your fantasies to interfere with your regaining your memory."

He looked quite unimpressed by this line of reasoning. "You said that when you found me, I was wearing expensive, if damaged, clothing. And this watch," he added, holding up his left wrist, where the watch rested above the burn marks, "would cost an ordinary yuppie a quarter of his annual salary."

"That's if it's real and not a good fake. Anyhow, it was a gift from Catherine. And I was guessing about the clothes, Ziggy."

"Fine, let's have it your way for the time being, Cherish," he answered impatiently. "I'm some impoverished sailor with a fondness for stuffed bunnies who wears hand-me-down designer clothes and fake wristwatches. Satisfied?"

"Do you think it's somehow more reasonable to assume that a total stranger who washed ashore in Belize with a knife wound is really a jet-setting millionaire with a diamond-covered mistress awaiting him at some first-class hotel and casino on the French Riviera?" she said in exasperation.

"I thought we were going to call a truce," he reminded her plaintively.

Cherish lowered her head and muttered an agreement. He was starting to look drawn and exhausted. If only he weren't so provoking!

In a tired voice, he asked, "Did you learn anything from the embassy?"

Cherish took a seat opposite Ziggy and rested her elbows on the table. "Not much," she admitted. "It took me over twenty minutes to get my first call through to them, then another twenty minutes to get someone there to talk to me."

"There's something so reassuring about bureaucracy. It remains the same, even when a man's forgotten everything else."

She smiled, even though she felt far from amused at the moment. The subject had finally come up; they would have to talk about it. "I reported your situation right away, then called back several hours later, after they'd had a chance to investigate. As far as they can tell, no one seems to be looking for you yet. They have no knowledge of any American woman named Catherine, and no other unidentified people have washed ashore.''

''I see.'' For once, he didn't look teasing or amused.

''The *Lusty Wench* is registered to an American citizen named Michael O'Grady.'' She swallowed nervously, wondering how to confront him with this. She started by asking, ''Does that sound familiar?''

''I . . . I don't know. No, I guess not. Not right now.''

Cherish took a deep breath before continuing. ''He's got a record as long as my arm, Ziggy, and he's served time only once. It had something to do with smuggling and selling antiquities on the black market.''

''I *know* this person?'' He eyed her disbelievingly.

She cleared her throat, meeting the open challenge in his expression. ''Well, you were wearing a life preserver that's apparently from his boat.''

Looking like he'd just tasted something bitter, Ziggy said, ''Can O'Grady be contacted, so he can identify me?''

''Unfortunately, no. He's recently been charged again, but he jumped bail three months ago and disappeared.''

''Now that's just great.'' Ziggy sat bolt upright, his gray eyes going wide as he stared at her. ''Wait a minute! Do you think *I'm* this O'Grady character?''

''The thought did cross my mind,'' she admitted carefully. ''But you don't fit the description. He's blond and blue-eyed.''

''Oh.'' He asked warily. ''Anything else you want to tell me?''

''It doesn't get any better,'' she warned him. ''The embassy in Belize City doesn't want to take responsibility for an unidentified man who can't *prove* he's American. Of course, if your memory doesn't return soon, they recommend you come to the embassy to be finger-printed.'' She waited for a response to that. His expression gave nothing away, so she continued, ''You may have been in the armed forces—''

''Or a federal prison?''

She shrugged uneasily. ''Anyhow, they recommend you wait until you're feeling better and have given your memory a chance to return.''

''In other words, you're stuck with me for the time being,'' he guessed.

She felt guilty, since this was exactly what she had been thinking, and it sounded so unfeeling. ''Well, 'stuck' is a little harsh—''

''Have you told your boss about me?'' When she nodded, he prodded for more information. ''What did he have to say about all this?''

''Uh, he, um . . .''

In fact, Grimly had said, ''What do you mean you're letting this rogue stay with you? Grow up, Dr. Love. No respectable person washes ashore with knife wounds and stuffed animals, without identification or memories. The scoundrel is probably a spy bent on stealing your research notes and claiming all the glory for himself. Get right back to Voodoo Caye and drown him!''

''Grimly didn't have many useful suggestions,'' Cherish said tactfully.

''He thinks you should kick me out, doesn't he?'' Ziggy surmised.

''He's, you know, concerned about the progress of my work.''

Really Grimly had said, ''Two days! Two *days* you've lost on account of this nameless bounder! What are you doing wasting even *more* time at Rum Point, Dr. Love?

Do you expect the Garifuna to do your research for you? Get back to work!''

"He thinks I'm dangerous," Ziggy guessed, studying her reddening face.

"Yes, but not to me, only to my research notes. Grimly's what you might call a bit obsessive about his work. If you aren't part of a disappearing culture, then you just aren't worth thinking about." She shrugged. "It's a little hard even for me to understand. Still, he's one of the most highly respected scholars in the world. Anyhow, his attitude toward you—or anyone else—isn't personal."

Ziggy grinned. "Yeah, my sister can be the same..." His jaw dropped and he shot out of his chair. "My sister!"

Cherish jumped up. "What? What? Tell me!"

Limping away from the table, his whole body radiating excitement, he said, "I...I have a sister. She's...she's... Oh, hell, I don't know!" He struck the wall with his fist.

"Calm down, don't try to force it. Let it come by itself," Cherish urged.

"Talking about academic types, research notes... It made me think of...I'm sure I...dammit, what's her name? What does she look like?"

But no more memories came, and Cherish saw he was bringing on another pounding headache with his desperate pursuit of the elusive vision. "Come on, Ziggy. Lie down. I'll clean your stitches, and then you can go to sleep. You're probably too tired to remember anything else tonight."

"What was I doing on the *Lusty Wench?* Where is it now? Why— Ow!" He closed his eyes against the sudden, stabbing pain in his head, bringing his fists up to his temples. "Oh, God," he groaned, his voice ragged and despairing.

"Come on, lie down." Cherish kept her voice low and soothing as she led him, stumbling, over to his hammock. Whatever her fears about Ziggy's background, she couldn't deny his obvious desire to remember who he was, or the very real pain he unleashed every time he thought about the night of the storm.

He fell back into the hammock at her gentle urging, making it swing wildly until she steadied it. She wondered if the ropes would be too rough against his many scratches and bruises, but one look at his expression told her that the pounding in his head and the torment of his thoughts had obliterated all minor discomforts from his consciousness.

She rinsed a cloth in cool water and placed it across his forehead to help ease the pain that had brought such terrible tension to his handsome face. In moments like this, when he let her see past his quick-tongued, teasing manner, it was impossible to ignore the warm tenderness that flooded her heart. When he was helpless and vulnerable like this, there was no denying the need to help him, to care for him, to comfort him.

His bare chest rose and fell with his sharp, agitated breaths as Cherish applied another cool cloth, this time to the wound on his shoulder, and stroked his hair soothingly. The chestnut waves were thick and luxuriant beneath her fingers, freshly scented from her own shampoo. In the golden glow of the lanterns, a faint gleam of sweat shone on the strong column of his throat when he tilted his head back. She removed the cloth from his forehead and wiped it gently down the length of his throat, hoping to ease his pain however she could.

He mumbled incoherently, and the darkening flush on his skin made her fear that his fever dreams would return if he continued to agitate himself.

"Shh. Ziggy, you must lie quietly," she whispered, putting her cloth aside and brushing his hair off his forehead.

He swallowed convulsively. "I can't. I..." Without warning, he grabbed her hand in a viselike grip and whispered harshly, "There's someone in the storm, someone out there who wants me dead...."

Her gaze moved from his face to his shoulder. She removed the damp cloth she had applied there and stared at the harsh wound and Granny's neat little stitches.

The washboard muscles of his stomach moved sinuously with his deep, ragged breaths. "Someone wants me dead," he repeated.

"Why?" she whispered, afraid for him.

"I don't know." His voice was hoarse as he tried to recall who hid in the cave of all his fears. His body trembled at an unknown danger that lurked in the shadows. Driven by instinct, by a primal fear of the impenetrable darkness in his own mind, he tugged on her hand. "Stay with me," he whispered.

A mingled thrill of fear and desire swept through her. "No. Your shoulder—"

"Stay with me," he insisted throatily, pulling her down with sudden strength. The hammock swayed alarmingly as her senses were assaulted by the musky scent of his skin, the heady feel of his legs tangling with hers, the warmth of his bare chest burning through her khaki shirt, the scratchy cotton of his shorts sliding against her thighs and the bristly roughness of his jaw as he turned his face into her neck.

"I'll hurt your—"

"No, you won't." He swallowed and his arm tightened painfully around her. Clearly striving for some semblance of control, he said in a voice whose unevenness betrayed him, "You don't have to stay with me all night. Just . . . for a bit. Till I fall asleep?"

That last request sounded almost pleading, and it was so unlike him that she agreed instantly, shifting to get comfortable with him in the swaying, sagging hammock. She hoped to God the fishing nets would continue to support their combined weight. Neither of them needed a sudden plummet to the hard wooden floor.

Despite his emotional agitation, Ziggy's healing body claimed sleep as its due within minutes. Cherish obliged him as he shifted in his sleep to pillow his head against her. He rested peacefully that way, with his arm around her waist, until well after midnight. It should have seemed ironic that having finally gotten her into bed, he was wasting the opportunity by sleeping like an exhausted puppy; but she found no irony in his vulnerability.

Oh, the chemistry between them was real enough, but flirting and seduction seemed to be almost second nature to Ziggy. As an anthropologist, Cherish theorized that that was how Ziggy had been socialized. He was much more comfortable with propositioning her than he was with asking for her help. From an objective, academic perspective, it seemed logical; he was a very attractive man, so most women he had encountered had undoubtedly encouraged him to communicate with them along sexual lines. Then, of course, the attitudes of his family, his social set and his age group all had to be taken into account, too. She wished she could ask him about those things.

Cherish sighed unconsciously as he nestled closer to her, and she rubbed her cheek against his thick hair. She could get used to this.

Ziggy's failure to respond appropriately to reprimands suggested he was generally rebellious. That, unfortunately, was not inconsistent with the suspicion that he traveled in felonious company. Crooks were often antisocial rebels, in any society.

She had felt sick when she had learned about the criminal, Michael O'Grady. Then learning that Ziggy didn't fit O'Grady's physical description had made her dizzy with relief. But the unpleasant truth was that Ziggy might be one of O'Grady's companions; he might perhaps be an even more dangerous man than O'Grady. Who wanted Ziggy dead, who had stabbed him and thrown him off the *Lusty Wench* in the middle of a storm?

Cherish grimaced with frustration. If only there was more information about O'Grady and the *Lusty Wench*. It was more imperative than ever that Ziggy regain his memory; the embassy official had warned her that the odds were against their being able to identify him by his fingerprints, in the event that his memory didn't return. He was too young to have been drafted, and Cherish frankly doubted that he had ever voluntarily submitted to military discipline. She dreaded the thought of identifying him by uncovering a criminal record.

But she had to know who he was because now his words would haunt her until they had solved the mysteries surrounding his presence on Voodoo Caye.

Someone wants me dead.

Five

He smelled burning eggs and coffee that was so brutally strong it woke him up. Oh, God, they must have let his sister Clowance into the kitchen again. The girl had never learned to cook, but one morning every year—on Father's birthday—they all pretended she could.

Father's birthday? Oh, damn, I forgot again. Why didn't Catherine remind me?

It was too early to work up a good case of guilt, though. He turned his face into the pillow and nuzzled something. It was small and fuzzy and limp. A stuffed animal. What was a stuffed animal doing in his bed?

He opened one bleary eye. A hideous, faded pink rabbit grinned back at him.

The bunny.

Ziggy sat bolt upright. The hammock swayed wildly, and the world turned upside down as he tumbled off the makeshift bed and hit the floor with a loud crash.

"Ziggy?" Cherish came rushing into the room through the open doorway of the ramshackle little cabin. "Did you hurt yourself?"

"Oh. Reality." From his prone position on the floor, Ziggy gave a heartfelt groan and threw his forearm over his eyes. "Oh, God, that sun is bright."

Cherish crouched down beside him. "Are you all right?"

Cold water dripped from her hair onto his chest. "You're all wet," he said accusingly.

"I'm washing my hair outside. I didn't want to wake you. You were sleeping so peacefully."

He looked up at her. How did the woman look so good wearing a faded, baggy shirt, with her hair dripping in soapy clumps, and her face flushed from holding her head upside down? He wanted to kiss her and touch her and unbutton that awful blouse. He wanted to finish washing her hair for her.

He wanted to tell her about his dreams and his nightmares and his darkest fears. And *that* was what made him lunge painfully to his feet and ask, "How did the bunny wind up in bed with me?"

"I crawled out of the hammock a couple of hours after you fell asleep. I figured I'd better finish cleaning up and blow out the lanterns. Anyhow, you got restless again and kept asking for the bunny, and you wouldn't quiet down until I gave it to you." She frowned at the stuffed animal and added, "I don't think that thing is very sanitary."

He remembered now. He'd fallen asleep in her arms. Feeling unaccustomedly shy, he asked, "Is that breakfast I smell?"

"Yes, I . . ." Her eyes popped open and she flew to the stove without her usual grace, flinging cold water and runny soap everywhere. "Oh, damn, damn, damn! I forgot about them!"

"You burned my eggs?" he guessed.

"Don't worry. I'll start over."

He didn't want to trouble her, considering all the trouble he'd already caused. "No, that's okay. I'll eat these."

"No, Ziggy, they're burned."

"It won't kill me," he lied. His stomach rebelled at the thought of solid food, even the appetizing kind—which didn't include Cherish's eggs.

"I'm sorry," she said, her soapy hair dripping into the eggs. "I don't cook very often."

"Something about this is very familiar," he said, still feeling disoriented as he peered into the pan. "The smells...I was dreaming." He nodded. "I think I have— or had—a family."

She went very still. Water ran from her cheeks, down her throat and into her shadowy cleavage. "A family? You mean a wife and children?"

"No, I mean parents. And a sister. And Catherine." He frowned, trying to pull together his spinning thoughts. "Yes, I think there *is* a Catherine in my life."

"Wife? Lover? Maiden aunt?"

He shrugged and ran a hand through his rumpled hair. "Who knows? She could be my damn dog, for all I know."

"Then she must be very well trained." Cherish glanced pointedly at his watch.

"Well, you know, former President Bush's dog wrote a book." He shook his head. "Why can I remember absurd things like that, but not my own name?" He felt like hitting something again.

"Well, at least you think there's a family who'll get worried about you and start making inquiries."

"Maybe." Not every family wanted to claim all its members. What kind of a son was he? What kind of a brother? "Maybe," he repeated gloomily, not at all sure.

"More things will come back to you, Ziggy. It's been only a couple of days." Her voice was patient, reassuring.

Her lips looked very pink, and her lashes stuck together in wet spikes. A bead of water trembled on the soft, pale swell of her breast, glistening against the perfect whiteness of her skin. "You don't have a tan," he sputtered suddenly.

She looked surprised at the sudden change of subject. "Well, no. I'm a redhead. I never go out in the midday sun without sunscreen and a hat. I'd turn into a lobster otherwise."

Realizing how rude he must have sounded, he said sincerely, "You have beautiful skin. Like mother-of-pearl."

She started flushing again. "Oh. Thank you, Ziggy." She lowered her eyes, those passionate green eyes that always gave her away. Didn't she know that she couldn't hide from her own nature? She might pretend to be reasonable and intellectual and celibate, but her eyes burned with sexuality and passion and temper. And sometimes, he recalled, they glowed with warmth and tenderness. Sometimes they were full of sympathy. Like last night.

It was his turn to flush and turn away. Humiliation washed over him as he remembered how he had trembled and whined like a child in the night, how he had begged her to stay with him. He hadn't wooed and won her, man to woman; he had been too afraid to be alone in the dark, and she had seen his weakness and comforted him. He couldn't say for sure, but he suddenly doubted that there had ever been a "morning after" more awkward than this one. Why hadn't he clenched his teeth and kept his babbling to himself? Why hadn't he made love to her and given her something to exchange for her comfort? Something about last night had been even more intimate than sex—for him, at least—and he didn't feel at all comfortable with it.

Cherish was still avoiding his eyes, trying to scrape his burned eggs out of the frying pan and onto a plate. He would give anything to simply pretend last night hadn't happened. However, he was a man, so it was up to him to face facts, face this woman, and put her at ease, even if he felt like he'd never find ease for himself again.

"Uh, Cherish. About last night?" His voice sounded husky and uncertain, embarrassing him.

"Yes?" she said over her shoulder, concentrating fiercely on not breaking an egg yolk that he figured could be used in a game of racquetball.

"I was...well, I mean, what I want to say is..." He gritted his teeth. What was the matter with him this morning? He always handled things much better than this.

That unbidden thought stopped him cold for a moment. He waited, but no other echo of the past came to him.

"Yes?" she prompted.

He met her gaze when she turned back to him. He was astonished to see that she now looked almost amused. She didn't really seem to be laughing at him. No, there was a softness about her, a warmth in her smile that made it impossible to take offense at the sparkle in her eyes. But she was definitely laughing in merry silence at *some-*

thing. It confused him and made him forget what he wanted to say.

"Are you feeling better now?" she asked.

He nodded. "I wanted to say... well, I'm sorry about last night." His voice was gruff.

"There's nothing to apologize for," she assured him, with that same gentle smile. "It's really not such a terrible side of you, Ziggy."

His glibness had deserted him completely, no doubt about it. Maybe he'd feel better after some coffee. He took the plate of eggs away from her and said, "You can go finish your hair, Doc. I'll, uh, you know, just, uh..."

She looked doubtfully at the eggs. "Look, I think I'll just give these to Dog-Dog, okay? God only knows what Granny will have to treat you for if you ingest these. Anyhow, I'm sure she has something she can spare for your breakfast."

"I'll go ask her," he said quickly.

"Not with that ankle, you won't." She pushed him toward a chair. "I know all this inactivity isn't making things any easier, Ziggy. I can see that you're not used to sitting around." Her gaze flicked down his leanly muscled form, and he wondered with unfamiliar humility if she liked his body. Some women liked a beefier guy, and some women liked men who were really skinny, or who had fewer scars or less chest hair. "But," she continued, turning quickly away, "you'll only delay your recovery if you try to do too much too soon. Once your ankle can comfortably take your weight, you can walk all over the island if it pleases you. Okay?"

Wanting to be alone more than anything, he said, "Okay."

She looked a little suspicious of his docility. Given his usual behavior, he supposed that was natural. Was he always such a contrary, unpredictable, moody guy, or was his association with this woman causing it? Of course, he reminded himself wryly, there was also that little matter of nearly dying and then waking up to a complete loss of memory. Yeah, something like that was bound to make a guy behave a little erratically.

The vague images he was starting to recall of a life before the storm intrigued him. He was so intent upon awakening more of those memories that he ignored the breakfast that Granny Martinez brought over, ignored the pain caused by her sterilization of his more severe wounds and even ignored the lingering bewilderment he felt over his sudden awkwardness around Cherish. Instead, he focused all his attention on trying to recall pleasant memories of incidents unrelated to the night of the storm, incidents that wouldn't cause that mixture of pain and panic that incapacitated and emasculated him.

Aromas had prompted this morning's memory, which he could only recall vaguely now. Something about a sister, a father, waking up in a safe place. A casual memory, nothing special or monumental. Exactly the kind of memories he needed in order to start putting the pieces together. He'd read somewhere—*where?*—that one's strongest memories were linked to the sense of smell. That inspired his plan.

Cherish left him alone in the cabin that day so she could go out and do some field research. Ziggy spent the time savoring every single scent and odor in and around the cabin, then letting himself do a little free association. As Cherish had suggested, it was hard to separate memory from fantasy—particularly when he caught a whiff of her body lotion—but the elusive, ordinary, nonthreatening images and flashes of familiarity started to come often enough to convince him that there was a chance that he'd eventually regain his memory. He was finally willing to believe that Cherish was right, that he had a "dissociative disorder" instead of brain damage. He didn't realize until now how terrified he'd been that he would never know who he was or where he belonged.

"What are you doing?" Cherish asked curiously, entering the cabin early that evening to find Ziggy sitting on the floor with an open jar of honey, a bulb of garlic and a bar of soap.

"Don't worry. It's not some deviant sexual practice," he said dryly. He explained what he'd been doing.

"That's a good idea." She sat down on one of the wooden chairs and crossed her legs. Those incredibly long, bare legs that had felt so smooth sliding against his own last night. He wondered if she had thought about it at all today, if she had enjoyed the feeling of their bodies fitting together so naturally. "Have you discovered any concrete memories yet?" she asked.

"No. Nothing concrete. But there's *something* locked up in my head." He closed his eyes, trying to concentrate. He wanted to give her a hug—to *get* a hug. He wanted to ask her what she'd been doing today, and what her field research entailed. Instead he said, "The welcome rug outside the front door smells like horses," he murmured. "I ride horses. I think I have, or *had,* an Arabian stallion. Black, very beautiful, short-tempered—"

"Are you sure? That's a very valuable horse, Ziggy."

"I know." He shrugged and let her think what she chose. "And I remember a woman...."

"Naturally." Her voice was dry.

"I think she was, you know, the *first* woman."

"And what smell made you remember that?" Cherish asked suspiciously.

He smiled, keeping his eyes closed. "It wasn't a smell, actually. It was seeing your hair tangled in your hairbrush. She was a redhead, like you, only older."

"How old were you?"

"I don't know. Young."

"And she was older than me?"

"Don't sound so shocked," he chided. "After all, who do you think teaches inexperienced young men to make love? Inexperienced young woman?"

"Actually that's a rather interesting subject. In some societies—"

Recognizing her academic lecturing tone, he interrupted, "Anyhow, I haven't remembered anything that could help us figure out who I am." His frustration vibrated in his voice.

After a slight pause, she said, "Listen, Granny thinks she has an idea that might help you."

"Does it involve boiled boa constrictor?"

"I'm not sure," she admitted. "I doubt it, though."

He gazed rather warily. "Go on."

"She wants to hold a *dugu*."

"By all means. Let her hold it, hug it, do whatever she wants with it. Who am I to judge?"

"This isn't a joking matter, Ziggy."

"Sorry."

She scowled at him, though she didn't look precisely angry. "I can see you're feeling better."

"Discovering I don't have brain damage always cheers me up."

Cherish sighed, but he thought he saw her trying to stifle a smile. He felt miles better than he had this morning. He was even almost able to forget what a coward he had been last night. Almost.

"A *dugu,* Ziggy, is the major ceremony in the Garifuna religion."

"I thought these people were Catholic."

"Catholicism and *dugu* coexist here."

"The ceremony?"

"The religion. The word stands for both things. *Dugu* beliefs combine Catholic, African and Carib Indian rituals. It uses fetishes, amulets, symbols. Not much popular work has been published on the subject, but if you'd like me to recommend several good—"

He interrupted before she could subreference him to death. "Why does Granny think this ceremony will help me?"

"It's a ritual to rid the community of evil spirits."

"So Granny still subscribes to the theory that evil spirits are the cause of my amnesia?" He hoped if he said the word *amnesia* aloud at regular intervals it would stop sounding so bad. Before Cherish could answer, he continued, "Granny's a wonderful woman and I wouldn't dream of ridiculing her religious beliefs. I mean that. But, Cherish, please tell me you're not going along with this. I mean, let's have a reality check here."

"It's not that, exactly." She started to look guilty.

"Then what?" When she didn't answer straight away, a terrible suspicion began to grow in his mind. "Tell me more about this *dugu* ceremony, Doc."

"It's a feast of reconciliation. It involves spiritual rituals, music, nonstop dancing, animal sacrifices—"

"Hey! Nobody is sacrificing a goat on *my* behalf," he protested.

"I don't know if it's a goat—"

"How many of these rituals have you seen, Cherish?"

"Uh, the actual number?"

"Uh-huh."

"Well...none," she admitted, looking with interest at the wall behind him.

"Why is that?" More silence. Dammit, he was right! "Could it be, Dr. Love, that since the *dugu* ceremony is a major religious ritual, outsiders generally aren't invited?"

Cherish cleared her throat and nodded.

"I can't believe this!" He glared at her. "You're using me as some kind of guinea pig!"

She hopped up. "I think that's a little extreme!"

"You're afraid you'll never get to see a *dugu* if you don't seize this opportunity. You've probably been thanking your lucky stars all day that I got stabbed and hit on the head and thrown off the *Lusty Wench!*"

"Ziggy," she said coldly, "I very much doubt that I will *ever* be grateful that you washed up on Voodoo Caye. However, since you're here, and since these very kind people want to help you, and since it would virtually assure me of more research funding if I could publish an account of the *dugu,* I think you'd have to be a heel to refuse!"

He stared at her for a tense moment, then said, "Do you know you're beautiful when you're angry?"

"Oh, really!" She stomped away from him.

"I actually meant that sincerely," he said to her empty chair. Cherish ignored him.

She continued to ignore him all through dinner, and she left him alone in the cabin—going stir-crazy—to take a walk on the beach at sunset. He fumed for a while, stalking aimlessly around the cabin, reassuring himself that he had a life somewhere, a life far away from Cherish Love and her anthropological obsessions. If only he knew where that life was, or who was a part of it.

He scowled at her when she came back to the cabin and went directly to her desk. After she had been writing in a notebook for twenty minutes, squinting in the lantern's glow, he said, ''If you think this silent treatment is going to make me change my mind, forget it, Cherish.''

''I would never do anything so manipulative,'' she responded scathingly.

''Oh, no?'' He peered over her shoulder. ''Then why have you been working on a single sentence for the past twenty minutes, unless the purpose of this exercise is specifically to keep your back to me?''

She slammed her notebook shut and rose to her feet with a thunderous expression. She met his knowing gaze and, without warning, started to laugh. ''All right. Touché,'' she said ruefully. ''I'm sorry. I've been acting like a spoiled child.''

''Yes, you have. Does the *dugu* mean that much to you?''

''Yes, it does.''

''Then why didn't you tell me that?''

''I did!''

''No, you didn't. You shouted something about research funding and told me what a heel I am.''

''Sorry,'' she muttered.

''You'll catch more flies with honey than with vinegar.'' His gaze traveled down her body. ''And I'm real partial to honey.''

''Stop it,'' she chided. ''I've already apologized.''

He grinned. ''I can't help myself. Basic instincts.''

''Nonsense. It's a question of socialization.''

''If I knew where I'd been socialized, we might be able to argue about it.'' Wanting her to understand that he could be coaxed but not bullied, he said, ''You could try just asking me to go along with this *dugu* because you want me to. As a favor.''

"A personal favor?'' She looked doubtful. ''This is about scholarship. I don't want to compromise—''

"Why not? Everything in the world is compromised, from sunup to sundown, from birth to death. Compromise yourself, Cherish. Bend a little.''

"I didn't know *you* were a philosopher.''

"You didn't ask,'' he replied. ''I'm developing a soft spot for you, Doc. So why don't you just ask me nicely, woman to man?''

"I don't ever ask for things woman to man,'' she said crisply.

"Then you're missing all the fun in life.''

"On the contrary. Not only is that kind of behavior unprofessional—''

"These are hardly professional circumstances.''

"But trading on my...my...''

"Your beauty? Your sex appeal?''

"Trading on my *gender* can only encourage men to believe they can...can... How can I put this delicately?''

"That they can have it off with you just because they've done you a favor?'' he guessed.

"You have *such* a way with words.''

"But that's the general idea?''

"Yes, that's the general idea.''

He sighed. ''Is that why you can't ask me nicely for a simple favor? Because you think that *I'd* then think that I'd have a right to jump your bones?''

"*Must* you be so colloquial?''

"Look, Cherish, I swear on the life of my mother— whoever she is—that if you and I... How can I put this delicately?''

"Oh, don't bother to try," she snapped.

"Anyhow, it won't be because I thought that you *owed* me or that I had a right. It'll be because you've said you want to." He moved closer and added wickedly, "You must already know that *I* want to."

"You are so difficult," she said through gritted teeth.

"Actually I'm easy. And I'm a veritable pushover for anthropologists with red hair."

"Ziggy, you're making my head hurt." She shoved him away. "Anyhow, why did you have to be so negative about the *dugu?* You make it sound like I'm asking you to do something awful."

"Animal sacrifice? Fetishes, amulets and nonstop dancing? And you haven't even told me what's on the music program. What if it's acid rock? Or opera?"

She blinked. "I think we're getting off the subject. The point is, I'm here to study these people, and there's nothing wrong with my wanting to use this opportunity to observe one of their most important communal rituals. You make it sound like I wanted to use you for something sleazy and immoral!"

"If only that were the case." She glared at him, and he held up his hands. "Okay, sorry. Sorry. I'll try to play straight man for a bit."

They stared silently at each other, suddenly realizing that they'd both run out of steam. At last, she said, "Will you sit down with Granny and at least discuss the *dugu?*" She licked her lips. "As a favor to me?"

He nodded and smiled slowly. "Sure, Cherish. Happy to." Unable to resist, he added, "You know, it's always good when we can talk things through like reasonable adults."

Six

The tropical night was long for Cherish, especially when she let herself think of the previous night, when she had lain wrapped in the arms of her infuriating, enervating, unpredictable houseguest. Of the five senses, he had reminded her, the sense of smell was perhaps the most evocative. She closed her eyes now and inhaled deeply, remembering the warm, male scent of his skin, the floral shampoo fragrance that clung to his hair, the rum that gave his breath a decadent perfume and the sharp masculine tang of sweat on his chest.

She had forbidden herself to think of these things all day, as she had forbidden herself the luxury of crying over his struggle with some unnamed, unknown danger. Most of all, she had forbidden the surge of aching tenderness she had felt when she had placed that awful stuffed bunny in his arms and watched him subside into restful sleep again.

She shouldn't feel so drawn to him, even though she was starting to recognize that all his flippancy and frivolity concealed a more serious nature than she had detected at first. He had tried to tell her something about himself tonight, though she still wasn't sure what, for he had remained elusive and jesting, enticingly skirting the edges of sincerity for a few moments.

What had he said? *Everyone is compromised, from sunup to sundown, from birth to death.*

She could hear his voice, like a whisper on the wind: *Bend a little.*

She sensed he was speaking of risks, of entering the whirlwind. He was bound to be disappointed, however. She was not a gambler, nor was she driven by instinct; she was a scholar, intellectual and methodical. That was the choice she had made.

The throaty call of the blue-crowned motmot intruded upon her thoughts, and Cherish turned over in the narrow confines of her cot to better catch the scents of the evening breeze. Jasmine, wisteria, hibiscus and oleander perfumed the air outside her window. How strange that she had never before noticed how subtly alluring their scents were, how suggestive they were of fertility. Of sensuality. Cherish hugged her pillow restlessly.

Maybe she should check on Ziggy, just to make sure he was breathing evenly and resting peacefully. He'd want to be awakened if he was having another one of those dreadful nightmares. She was halfway to the door before she stopped herself, recognizing the pathetic excuse for precisely what it was. She just wanted to look for trouble, with the man who invited it more than any man she'd ever known.

She turned instead and let her footsteps guide her to the window, where she leaned upon the windowsill and gazed up at the sliver of moon, which glowed like a magic jewel against the dark blue velvet of the Voodoo sky.

"A sickle moon," she murmured.

"It looks like we could reach right up and steal it, doesn't it?" Ziggy said behind her.

Her body tensed, and she wondered if her thoughts had called him here. "I thought you were asleep," she whispered over her shoulder.

"No. Couldn't sleep. I was out on the porch, wishing I could go down to the beach."

"Oh."

"I heard you moving around and came to make sure you're all right."

"I'm all right." He was only a silhouette in the doorway, tall and broad shouldered. She couldn't see his expression, but the tension in his body spoke volumes.

"I know you're all right," he admitted. "That's not really why I came in here, Cherish."

Nor, she guessed, had he come to seduce her, despite the scented beauty of the night. Realizing he needed encouragement, she asked, "Are you—do you want to talk?"

"No." After a heavy pause, he admitted slowly, "I just wanted company. I don't want to be alone."

"The nights are hard for you," she murmured.

"I feel like a little kid afraid of monsters in his closet."

She could guess what it had cost him to tell her that. "Why don't you lie down for a while? I'll sit with you."

He made a sound that might have been a puff of laughter. "Who'd have guessed that that would be exactly what I'd want on a moonlit night in the tropics with a beautiful woman?"

"Well, I realized early on that you're anything but predictable." And though she couldn't see his face, she knew he smiled in return.

Early the following morning, Granny came by with breakfast and explained the *dugu* ceremony to Ziggy. He looked doubtful, but Granny didn't seem to mind, and he was scrupulously polite. It was only after Granny left that Cherish noticed just how thoroughly disreputable Ziggy looked. She couldn't do anything about his clothes—another pair of her shorts and a bright shirt he'd borrowed from Peter Sacqui—but she could definitely do something about the heavy five o'clock shadow that was fast turning into a beard.

"How about a shave?" she suggested.

He ran a hand along his stubbly jaw. "Good idea. I feel like shag carpeting. Have you got a razor?"

"I bought a two-year supply. For my legs."

He warily eyed the dainty pink instrument she unwrapped with a flourish a few moments later. "I don't think it's quite the same thing as what I use, Cherish."

"A razor blade is a razor blade. If this one can handle two whole legs, it can certainly deal effectively with your cheeks, Ziggy. And look! I've even got shaving cream."

"I know. Lemon scented." He started to get out of the chair.

Cherish pushed him firmly back in place. "Now just sit still. This won't hurt a bit."

"I'll do it," he insisted.

"With those raw wrists and scratched hands and that bad shoulder?"

"I'm not an invalid." His expression clouded momentarily, as it always did when he looked at the inexplicable marks on his wrists.

"Give me a chance, Ziggy. I used to shave my grand-father."

He looked doubtful but resigned. Until, that is, she started slathering her shaving cream on his face. "Don't put that stuff on my face. No, don't! Aw, Cherish!" He sneezed.

"Do you make this much of a fuss at the barber's?" she chided.

"I can't remember," he grumbled.

After a little more insistence on her part, he subsided into his chair and permitted her to lather him. "You needn't look like such a martyr," she admonished.

His long-suffering expression was replaced by a flash of irritation. "Surely it's enough that I'm permitting you to make me look like lemon meringue pie and then hold a pink razor against my throat. I refuse to also pretend I'm enjoying the experience."

In truth, Cherish didn't know why she had insisted on doing this herself. The idea had simply been too enticing to resist. Perhaps now that he was healing so well and growing so much stronger, she simply sought a new excuse to touch him. Despite his many character defects, he was undeniably pleasant to touch.

"Your eye is looking much better today," she said. The swelling was gone, and the bruises were starting to fade. "And that ointment Granny gave me has really helped this big scratch on your face." Nevertheless, she was extremely careful when shaving the right side of his face.

"My ankle feels pretty good this morning, too." He obligingly tilted his chin in response to the pressure of her hand. "Ouch."

"Sorry." She moved closer to his side and frowned in concentration. "So what do you think about the *dugu?*"

He shrugged his good shoulder. "I'm willing to go along with it. Granny says that since it's being done on such short notice, it'll only last a day and a night, instead of a whole week, which is the usual length."

"Oh." She tried to hide her disappointment. He noticed it, however, and pinched her sharply, making her gasp in indignation.

"You didn't tell me you were thinking of a ceremony that would last a *week,* Doc."

"Well . . ."

"Look on the bright side. If it weren't for me, this wouldn't be happening at all. Right?" She shrugged and moved to his other side. Looking curious, he said, "Everyone around here speaks English in that singsong Caribbean way, but I don't recognize the language they use with each other. Who are these people, anyhow?"

"The Garifuna? Well, their ancestors were West Africans who escaped from a seventeenth-century slave ship that ran aground off a tiny Caribbean island near St. Vincent. They intermarried with the indigenous Carib Indians there and gave birth to a unique culture."

"St. Vincent? That's quite a distance. How did they wind up here?"

"Hold still," she instructed when he tried to look at her. "They resisted English colonization until the late eighteenth century, when their chief was killed and their rebellion was crushed. They were deported to the Bay Islands off Honduras, which was then a part of the British empire." She rinsed her razor and continued, "In the nineteenth century the Garifuna started drifting north along the coast and islands of Central America."

"So there are Garifuna throughout Central America?"

GET 4 BOOKS
A CUDDLY TEDDY
AND A MYSTERY GIFT

Return this card, and we'll send you 4 Silhouette Desires,
absolutely FREE! We'll even pay the postage and packing for you!

We're making you this offer to introduce to you the benefits of
Silhouette Reader Service: FREE home delivery of brand-new
Desire romances, at least a month before they're available in the
shops, FREE gifts and a monthly Newsletter packed with offers
and information.

Accepting these FREE books places you under no obligation to
buy, you may cancel at any time, even after receiving just your
free shipment.

Yes, please send me 4 free Silhouette Desires, a cuddly teddy
and a mystery gift as explained above. Please also reserve a
Reader Service subscription for me. If I decide to subscribe, I
shall receive 6 superb new titles every month for just £11.40
postage and packing free. If I decide not to subscribe I shall
write to you within 10 days. The free books and gifts will be
mine to keep in any case. I understand that I am under no
obligation whatsoever. I may cancel or suspend my
subscription at any time simply by writing to you.

Ms/Mrs/Miss/Mr ⎯⎯⎯⎯⎯⎯⎯⎯⎯⎯⎯⎯⎯⎯ 6S4SD

Address ⎯⎯⎯⎯⎯⎯⎯⎯⎯⎯⎯⎯⎯⎯⎯⎯⎯⎯⎯

⎯⎯⎯⎯⎯⎯⎯⎯⎯⎯⎯⎯⎯⎯⎯⎯⎯⎯⎯⎯⎯⎯⎯⎯

⎯⎯⎯⎯⎯⎯⎯⎯⎯⎯⎯ Postcode⎯⎯⎯⎯⎯⎯⎯

Signature⎯⎯⎯⎯⎯⎯⎯⎯⎯⎯⎯⎯⎯⎯⎯⎯⎯⎯⎯
I am over 18 years of age.

Get 4 books
a cuddly teddy and
mystery gift FREE!

SEE BACK OF CARD FOR DETAILS

Silhouette Reader Service,
FREEPOST
P.O. Box 236
Croydon
CR9 9EL

Offer expires 31st December 1994. One per household. The right is reserved to refuse an application and change the terms of this offer. Offer applies to U.K. and Eire only. Offer not available for current subscribers to Silhouette Desires. Readers overseas please send for details. Southern Africa write to: IBS Private Bag X3010, Randburg 2125. You may be mailed with offers from other reputable companies as a result of this application.

If you would prefer not to receive such offers, please tick this box. ☐

No
stamp
needed

"Yes, but they're primarily concentrated here in Belize. Besides all these island communities, there are several sizable towns on the Belizean mainland that are primarily Garifuna."

She moved to stand between his legs so she could shave his chin. "The Garifuna have a strong pride in their heritage, and they have recorded their culture and history. But isolated, traditional communities like this one on Voodoo Caye are becoming rare. Tilt your head up."

"How did you wind up here?" Ziggy asked, adjusting his position so that his knees bracketed her legs. "I mean, not every girl starts out her college education with the idea that she's going to spend her career on an island with no telephone or five-star restaurants so that she can study a group of people that most Americans have never heard of."

She smiled and admitted, "When Grimly first hired me, it took my poor mother a week to find a map with Voodoo Caye on it. And my father had so much trouble remembering *who* I'm studying that he's finally resorted to keeping the word 'Garifuna' written on a slip of paper in his wallet."

Ziggy smiled, too—cautiously, since she hadn't quite finished with his chin. "What qualified you for the job?"

"I'm *very* qualified." Cherish stiffened slightly. "I have a PhD in anthropology, I graduated at the top of my class, my dissertation was a study of cultural displacement resulting from the African slave trade, I—"

"Slow down, Doc." He increased the pressure of his knees against her legs and pulled her forward. "I wasn't questioning your credentials. I simply meant, what are you doing *here* instead of some other backwater favored by anthropologists?"

"Oh. I see."

Ziggy put his hands on her waist. "A little touchy, aren't we?"

"Sorry." She looked away. "I think you're all shaved. You look acceptable."

"Acceptable? Wow! Thanks. How many women, I wonder, have paid me a compliment like *that?* I'll try not to let it go to my head."

She had to smile. "Okay. Better than acceptable. Actually, without that beard, and now that your face is healing, you look pretty good. You're probably a regular heartbreaker back home."

"Wherever that is."

"Yes."

"Why are you so defensive about your qualifications?"

She sighed. "What's the use? You're a man."

"That's right." He grinned and pulled her so close that his chest pressed against her belly. She dropped the razor on the floor. He looked up into her face. "And if you still have doubts, I'd be happy to set you straight."

"I meant that a woman would get it, but you're probably genetically incapable of understanding."

"Try me." His arms tightened when she tried to pull away. She pushed against his shoulders, then felt immediately contrite when the action made him wince. He didn't loosen his hold, however. Giving up, Cherish let him pull her down onto his lap.

"Well?" he asked.

Hotly aware of his hard thighs beneath her buttocks, the muscular arm pressing against her back, and the hand resting with deceptive casualness at her waist, Cherish looked into those ever-changing gray eyes. His face really did look remarkably good now. Without the stubble and the injuries, his strongly sculpted bones, sun-kissed skin, full lips, arching brows and thick lashes made him look both rakish and aristocratic, like the sensitive, recklessly gallant heroes of her adolescent fantasies. However, Ziggy was rather less poetic and considerably more lascivious than the heartthrobs she had created in her girlhood daydreams. She pointedly shoved away the hand that was sliding across her waist to caress her stomach with subtle skill.

"*This* is precisely what makes me so defensive," Cherish said tersely.

"Do you mean you don't like being touched?" He went still and frowned questioningly into her face.

"I don't like being ogled, fondled, harassed, pawed and pestered," she corrected coldly.

He stared at her for a moment. Then, with a carefully blank expression, he pushed her gently out of his lap and stood up. He crossed the room and pretended to study his face in the tiny mirror above the kitchen sink—the only mirror Cherish kept in her cabin. "Do all men produce this reaction in you, or is it me in particular?"

"Would it make a difference?" she asked wearily, slouching into the chair he had just vacated.

He looked over his shoulder. "Believe it or not, it would."

"Why? In what way?" She shook her head, not giving him a chance to respond. "Men want one thing only, Ziggy. I figured that out when I was fourteen. Every boy in school wanted to date me. Not because I was intelligent—"

"I don't know how to break this to you, Dr. Love, but no teenage boy *ever* wants to date a girl because she's intelligent."

"Not because they liked my personality," she continued to say, doggedly, "or because they thought I might be fun to be with. Not even because I took good geometry notes or might be a good listener. No, every boy wanted to date me because I was the 'really built' redhead with 'the great big jugs.'"

Ziggy winced. "I can see how that wouldn't endear my sex to you. But, Cherish, that was high school. Surely since then—"

"Now who's being naive?" she said interrupting him. "If anything, it got worse at college, with hormonal young men who were free of their parents' supervision for the first time ever. And they were all just *sure* that a girl with a name like Cherish Love would 'put out.'"

"How'd you get a name like that, anyway?"

"It's my mother's fault. And someone called 'Ziggy' is in no position to be critical."

"No," he agreed. He moved restlessly around the little cabin, testing his healing ankle, avoiding her eyes. "I guess I've never thought about this from your... from a woman's point of view." He rotated his bad shoulder experimentally a few times as he spoke. "And I can't say for sure, because I can't remember being nineteen or twenty, but I probably would have wanted to date you for all the same reasons. Although I hope," he added with a touch of disdain, "that I would have had better taste than to compliment your 'great big jugs' and ask you to 'put out.'"

"I'm sure you would have been very smooth, Ziggy." It wasn't precisely a compliment. "Looking like, you know, like a *pinup* girl..." She gave him a pointed look.

"Sorry," he muttered.

"Well, it's not all it's cracked up to be."

He glanced back into the mirror and tried to lighten the mood. "Funny, I really like being devilishly handsome."

She tried not to smile. "Sure, but you can walk past a construction crew in perfect safety." She sighed. "Why do men always think a woman should be flattered by every offer to be impregnated by a total stranger?"

"Well, when you put it that way..." He sat in a chair opposite her and said with rare seriousness, "Do I have things to apologize for, Cherish?"

She was surprised. "You're not responsible for every man who's ever pinched my butt or described the size of his—"

"No, I know that. I was thinking of apologizing for myself."

"Oh." She blinked, not sure how to respond. She was astonished to realize that she didn't feel a desire to hear him apologize to her for his persistent flirting, hot kisses, personal questions and outrageous suggestions.

It made no sense. Hadn't she, only a couple of days ago, lumped Ziggy into the same category with every other man who'd ever made an uninvited and unwanted pass at her? Yet now, as he tentatively offered an apology, she realized she felt no resentment about the often teasing, usually reckless, occasionally annoying, frankly charming and relentlessly sexual game of cat and mouse that had ensued between them ever since his arrival.

When she didn't respond, he said gently, "Is that what makes you so determined to be acknowledged professionally? Have you endured a lot of sexual harassment on the job?"

"Oh, it's more than that. It's everyone's assumption that a woman who looks like I do must have the IQ of cabbage."

He started to laugh, then realized she was serious. "Come on. Can anyone who's talked to you really think that? I mean, it's obvious that you're—"

"Obvious to who?"

"To me."

"Then I wish *you* were the chair of some college anthropology department." And suddenly, she found herself pouring out her heart to him, telling him things she was unaccustomed to sharing with anyone. She had listened to his feverish ramblings and held his nightmares at bay, and perhaps that had created a bond between them. Or perhaps she had simply misjudged him, for now Ziggy listened to her with a thoughtful sympathy she wouldn't have expected of him a couple of days ago.

"They denied you the grant because of the way you looked?" he asked incredulously at one point. "I don't understand."

"I could never prove discrimination. I only heard about the reasons for their decision through the grapevine, and they did actually give the grant to another woman. But the *questions* they asked me at the final interview!"

"Like what?"

"Like, was I aware that the research site I proposed was very isolated, that I wouldn't have access to the comforts I was accustomed to? That my social life would be curtailed? That I would be expected to observe local customs?" She snorted. "Of course I knew those things!" She shook her head and continued wearily. "But I found out later that one of the committee members actually said that she doubted I could bear to live more than three blocks away from a cosmetics counter, and who *knew* what would happen if something went wrong with my breast implants! I mean, *really*, Ziggy. When you met me, did you think I had implants?"

He glanced appreciatively at her breasts and replied, "No. I'm not an expert, but I never thought they were anything but real, Cherish."

"And the rest of the committee apparently agreed that my physical appearance would interfere with my ability to do my research."

"In other words, you were too pretty to be a good field researcher?"

"Yes, and I couldn't possibly be accustomed to going a whole year without sex," she added with disgust.

"I wonder if I am?" he said pensively.

"I'm not some kind of walking one-woman bordello. I can certainly go a year without sex. I've gone longer."

"I wonder if I have." He shuddered at the thought, then returned to the subject at hand. "Forget about them, Cherish. It was envy on the part of the women and wishful thinking on the part of the men."

"Wishful thinking?" she repeated with a sneer. "That must be what makes married men old enough to be my father think I should be willing to accommodate them. The following year I was considered for a position at Barrington University, where—"

"Wait a minute! Barrington? That's familiar."

"It is?" She forgot her grievances and asked, "Do you just recognize the name? Or did you go there?" She thought again of his elegant Ivy League accent. Maybe his flashes of memory weren't so improbable. Maybe he really did come from a privileged background and had been well educated.

After a moment of tense silence, he shook his head. "I don't know. Hell, maybe I was thrown out of Barrington, or maybe I knew a girl there. Nothing's coming to me." After another moment, he gave it up and prompted, "I take it you never got the job at Barrington?"

She rolled her eyes. "No. The chairman of the department got me alone in his office for an interview, then made a very heavy-handed pass. I was so offended I beaned him with a Dogon death mask and damaged it beyond repair. Damaged him a bit, too."

"I can see how that pretty well scotched your chance of getting the job," he said dryly. "Did you file a complaint?"

"Yes, but without much hope. It was his word against mine. The respected, much-published head of the department *versus* some 'bimbo' who'd just been rejected for the position."

"Too bad he wasn't stupid enough to pester you in front of witnesses."

"That's one of the difficulties with sexual harassment. It can be so hard to prove." She shrugged. "My complaint is probably still wandering through the maze of bureaucracy at Barrington."

"But you had the last laugh. You got this job. And, I'm forced to admit, Voodoo Caye isn't such a bad place, even though I'd love to see a Lakers game. Hey! What time of year is it?"

"February. Are you a Lakers fan?"

"Absolutely! In fact, I've got tickets for the—" He stopped and stared.

"What were you going to say?"

He looked bewildered. "I don't know. Things start to come out on their own, but the second I become aware of what I'm saying—" he made a gesture "—it's gone."

"More will come," she assured him.

"It's so damn frustrating!" He brought his fist down on the table, causing it to shake.

"I know." Full of empathy, grateful for his sympathetic understanding, she covered his fist with her hand.

He took a deep breath, and she could feel the tension ease slowly out of him as he opened his fist and laced his fingers with hers. "Better?" she asked.

"Yeah." He studied their linked hands for a while before asking, "When will you go to the mainland to phone the embassy again?"

"The day after the *dugu*."

"I should be fit enough to go there in person soon."

Her stomach contracted. "Yes."

"If they fingerprint me..." He turned his other hand over, examining his callused palm. "I wonder what they'll find out."

"Maybe nothing."

"Maybe I've got a criminal record."

She couldn't deny it. She added quietly, "Maybe you've got a wife named Catherine."

"Maybe," he agreed with a careful lack of expression. "You'd think I'd have a wedding ring, though."

"A lot of married men don't wear one."

He shrugged. "I wonder how Catherine will feel about being forgotten?"

Cherish slowly pulled her hand out of Ziggy's grasp. "I—have work to do. I want to observe Granny's preparations for the *dugu*. This is a wonderful opportunity..."

"Uh-huh."

"Will you be all right today?"

"Yeah. I feel pretty good. I think I'll wander around the village, get some air. Maybe go down to the beach later."

"Okay."

She paused at the doorway, watching him as he went over to the sink to wash up after his shave. Leaving him alone was much harder than she wanted it to be.

Seven

"What are you doing?" Cherish asked Luke one afternoon the following week, interrupting his game with a dozen other island children.

"Playing basketball," he informed her, beaming. "Ziggy showed us how. He's our coach!"

"Is he, indeed?" Cherish asked darkly. This was just one of many incidents during the past four or five days that indicated that Ziggy's presence on Voodoo Caye, now that he was mobile and almost fully recovered from his injuries, was having quite a remarkable impact on the locals. It was time they talked about it. She should have laid down some ground rules days ago, right after discovering he had started teaching a virtual encyclopedia of American slang to the women. "Do you know where he is?"

"Ziggy said he was going down to Indigo Beach for a swim," Luke answered. "Want to see me slam-dunk one hard?"

"Not just now, Luke. When I get back, okay?"

"Right on!"

Cherish winced and set off for the beach where she had originally found Ziggy.

Ziggy stood at the water's edge, wearing only a faded pair of boxer shorts Cherish had given him days ago. For the hundredth time, he resolved to dive into the next wave; for the hundredth time, he failed. Every time he thought of immersing himself in the sea, he felt a wave of terror so fierce it nauseated him. When it eased, his shame kept his stomach churning. Between that, Cherish's cooking and his suspicion of any food Granny Martinez placed before him, was it any wonder that he had lost a little weight?

"Next wave," he promised himself.

He was instinctively sure he knew how to swim. The fact that he had survived the storm helped confirm it. He even had a feeling that he had, prior to that night, enjoyed swimming. But now, as the next wave approached the shore, he was filled with blinding horror.

The pain. The blood. A shark. Another mouthful of salt water. Driven under the waves again, clutching the bunny. Nearly losing the life preserver.

He closed his eyes and shuddered, trying to breathe through a tight throat as he listened to yet another wave break. Hell, maybe he should just give up and go back to the cabin.

No, Cherish might be there. He'd been trying to give her a wide berth since the morning she'd explained exactly how many good reasons she had to despise men who couldn't keep their hands off of her. He doubted she had meant it personally, and she had certainly brushed aside the opportunity to make him apologize.

He certainly had no intention of insulting her, forcing himself on her, or embarrassing her as so many others had done; but the truth was, he didn't think he could keep his hands off her much longer. Living with her was straining his self-control to the limit.

Every morning she wandered into the kitchen in some plain, baggy, shapeless, faded cotton thing. It made his mouth water. It made his belly clench. Did she know that so many washings had made it sheer? When the rays of the sun peeked through a window or door and highlighted her rumpled red hair, her sleep-softened green eyes and her alabaster skin, did she know that the light also flowed through the tight weave of that nightgown, revealing the curve of her hips and the exciting V where her legs came together? Did she know that he had lost sleep over the round shadow of her navel and the darkly hinted shades of her areolae? Did she suspect that he'd left the cabin before she awoke this morning because *yesterday* morning he'd had such a hell of a time trying to conceal his physical response from her? That was one sign of his increasingly good health that he didn't think would please her.

Another wave approached the shore. *This* one he'd dive into; he needed a good dash of cold water right now.

Death. Water. Blood.

He watched the wave break against the shore.

The nights were sheer torture. He endured the intimacy of watching her tidy up the cabin as she prepared for bed, seeing her return from the ablution block out back all lush and damp, and listening to her shuffle around her bedroom. The gentle sway of his hammock and the scented island breezes tormented him almost as much as the soft rustle of Cherish's sheets and the little sighs she sometimes gave in her sleep.

But the *worst* was surviving her unannounced visits to him in the middle of the night. It was embarrassing enough that she knew how the darkness panicked him and gave power to his nightmares. There was no point in pretending otherwise; she'd held him in her arms to shield him from his own demons, and sat by his side to keep his monsters at bay. But her gentle presence at his bedside, her silent visits to ensure he was all right, only made it harder to suffer the rest of the night without her. His need for her had gone beyond the desire for comfort and companionship, another person in the darkness, a friend in an unknown universe.

He wanted her as a woman, as a lover. He wanted her skin beneath his palms, her body entwined with his, her legs wrapped around him. He wanted the wordless sounds of her pleasure, the sweet sighs of her satisfaction, the intimate whispers of her pillow talk.

And she wanted to be left alone. Never mind the tenderness he sometimes saw in her eyes. Forget about the flash of desire she sometimes couldn't conceal when they bumped into each other in the little cabin. Those moments were always followed by a quick recovery. She wanted to suppress her own nature, and he doubted he could change her mind by behaving like every other man who'd ever panted after her, uninvited and unwanted.

Surely he had enough problems to worry about already. Despite his brief flickers of memory, he knew nothing more concrete about himself than he had known upon awakening on Voodoo Caye to discover he didn't even know his own name.

There was only one thing he was completely sure of. Someone wanted him dead.

She found him standing at the water's edge, staring out across the ocean as if the answer to all his questions could be found on the horizon. He was bare-chested, and she noticed that his tan had darkened slightly in recent days. His shirt lay in a little heap on the beach, weighted down by the stuffed bunny. He seldom let that thing out of his sight, though he said he still couldn't remember its significance.

He'd been moody for the past few days, offering only flippant comments or impersonal courtesy to break his long silences. Not that she saw him much, anyhow, now that he was mobile. She supposed he was sick of her company. Certainly he had spent more time with virtually everyone else on Voodoo Caye than he'd spent with her since the morning she'd opened up to him.

Maybe he didn't like a complainer. She shouldn't have poured her heart out like that. Or maybe he had curtailed his teasing comments and familiar touches because of what she had revealed. She supposed she should be glad. In a way, that must have been her goal in telling him about her troubles. However, now that he was behaving with such propriety, she wanted to shake him till his teeth rattled and tell him to stop being so bloody polite. He could be the model of courtesy and Emily Post correctness when he wanted to, but Cherish thought it didn't suit him at all. And it certainly didn't agree with *her.*

Polite or not, there was no reason he had to avoid her like the plague, was there? Last night he hadn't come home from Peter Sacqui's cottage until very late, and this morning he had left before dawn. Was Cherish's company so intolerably dull? Was it such torture to share a pot of coffee with her in the morning? She had thought, if nothing else, that they had grown to like each other.

She might even actually have eventually admitted to becoming rather fond of Ziggy.

But now that she had irrevocably labeled sex as out-of-bounds, he was showing her about as much warmth as a glacier.

Men.

Her irritation grew by leaps and bounds as she stalked toward him under the azure-blue sky, removing her shoes and letting the sand trickle through her bare toes.

"I have to talk to you," she announced.

He nearly jumped out of his skin. "Dammit, Cherish! What are you doing sneaking up on me like that?"

"*Sneaking?* What are you doing staring at the water like you're in a trance?"

"I'm . . . getting ready for a swim."

"Oh. So sorry to interrupt your leisure, but this is important."

"Do I detect a touch of sarcasm in your voice, Dr. Love?"

"More than that," she warned. "I'm very angry, Ziggy."

"What is it now?"

His absentminded tone irked her. "You've got to stop your interference with the Garifuna."

He finally gave her his full attention. "What are you talking about?"

"What am I talking about?" she repeated incredulously. "You are contaminating this culture!" He frowned blankly at her. She huffed with exasperation. "You're poisoning their language with American slang. You're teaching them sports and card games that are alien to their traditions. And today I heard that you've been encouraging some of them to develop Voodoo Caye for tourism. How *could* you?"

"You're spoiling for a fight, aren't you?" he snapped.

"Don't change the subject!"

"Fine. Let me get this straight. You want to know how I could have the nerve to be friendly to all the people here who've been so nice to me?"

"Being friendly is quite a different thing from interfering with their traditional culture."

"Yeah, it would sure be nice for you if they could stay frozen forever, without ever changing, wouldn't it, Doc? Then you could spend the rest of your career getting famous by publishing scholarly articles about them."

"This has nothing—"

"This has everything to do with it. You don't want what's best for them. You want what's best for *you*."

"Don't get sanctimonious on me—"

"Look who's talking!"

"You're just bored and making mischief!"

"And you're just blind to reality. You've spent too long in that ivory tower of yours, Doc. Sometimes you remind me so much of C...Cl..." He trailed off, his expression changing as shock washed across his face and he struggled with the elusive memory.

"Of who?" she asked quickly. "Catherine?"

He shook his head. "No. That's not it. It's Clo..."

"Chloe? Claire? Clyde?" she prompted.

He squeezed his eyes shut. "I want to strangle her sometimes. But I love her."

"Wife? Sister? Girlfriend?"

Eyes still closed, he murmured, "Sister? Sister, I think. Maybe." After a few more seconds he opened his eyes. "It's gone."

"That's twice that something, uh, academic has made you think of her," Cherish said thoughtfully, deciding to forget about their quarrel for now. He looked depressed, and perhaps she had already made her point. Anyhow, she didn't have the heart to criticize him when he had lost all interest in fighting back, as he obviously just had. "I think I'll leave you alone for your swim now. Unless you'd like me to stay on the beach in case—"

"No, thanks. That's okay," he said gruffly. "Go back to watching Granny do whatever she's doing."

"Are you ready for the *dugu* tomorrow?"

"Ready as I'll ever be." He sounded despondent.

Feeling a little worried about him, she turned and left. She looked over her shoulder only once, when she was entering the jungle path that led to the village and the other side of the small island. He was still standing at the water's edge, staring into the waves.

She lay in the darkness for a long time that night, angry at him for once again coming home long after she'd already gone to bed, and worried about his mental state. He'd been on Voodoo Caye for over a week now, and she was starting to believe that his memory simply wouldn't return to him without familiar stimulants.

But what would be familiar to him? She had felt skeptical about his announcement earlier in the week that he thought he drove a red Porsche back home—wherever that was. Nor did she have overwhelming confidence in his recently stated belief that he had dined occasionally at Maxim's in Paris and stayed more than once at the Ritz in London.

However, she had reached the point where testing these theories sounded better than doing nothing. But how? Ziggy had washed ashore without a penny, and Cherish certainly couldn't afford to send him to Paris or London to see if anyone at Maxim's or the Ritz recognized him. Besides, he couldn't go anywhere without a passport.

She sighed and rolled over. She would phone the American Embassy again, the day after tomorrow. Maybe they had something to report. If not, she decided, she would talk to Ziggy and see if, now that he was fit and well, the two of them could develop a more aggressive plan of action to discover his identity. The sooner he was off Voodoo Caye and away from the Garifuna, the better.

It was funny how the thought of his longed-for departure simply put her in a worse mood. She buried her face in her pillow and resolved not to check on him tonight.

By sunset the following day, Ziggy was pretty glad he'd agreed to the *dugu*. For one thing, everyone was clearly having a hell of a time, particularly Granny Martinez. He supposed even Cherish would be having fun, if she could only bring herself to stop taking notes for five minutes. Granny had forbidden photography at the ceremony, so Cherish was writing down not only the details of the rituals and dancing, but also a thorough description of every costume, amulet and food offering in sight. Just watching her made Ziggy weary.

It also made his chest ache. He had wished she would stop checking on him at night, but now he felt wounded because she'd left him completely on his own last night. Which just proved, he supposed, that the old saying was true: when the gods want to punish us, they answer our prayers. His reaction wasn't rational, but then, Cherish Love didn't exactly inspire rationality in him even at the best of times.

And last night had definitely not been the best of times. He shouldn't have spent so much time staring at the damn ocean yesterday. His dreams had been a horror chamber of nameless fears. He had longed for the touch of Cherish's hand on his forehead, her soothing presence by his side, the soft murmur of her voice. Hell, if he was honest, he'd admit that he had longed to bury himself in her body and lose himself in her embrace.

"Drink up, Ziggy!" Peter Sacqui urged, slapping him on the back.

Ziggy obliged, downing the rest of his mug of the potent brew that flowed so freely today. Head swimming, he reached down to pet Dog-Dog, who panted nervously at all the unfamiliar chanting, drumming, singing and dancing in the crowded village square.

"A *dugu* sure is noisy," Ziggy observed.

"Ahh, that's so the spirits can hear us," Peter explained.

"Do *you* think I'm infested with evil spirits?"

"Hey, I don't know, Ziggy. Maybe it's just that your memory needs to be called back to your body. Maybe it went looking for something."

Ziggy frowned. "What would it have gone looking for?"

"A past life. An old enemy. A friend who needs it more than you do." Peter shrugged. "Maybe it has gone to find you a mate."

"Or maybe it's running away from one I've already got somewhere," Ziggy said gloomily.

Peter laughed. "Or maybe," he continued, warming to his subject, "your memory left to save your life."

"How so?"

"Well, whoever stabbed you isn't gonna find you on Voodoo Caye. No one knows you're here, and we'd all spot a stranger on the island long before he could get to you. So you're safe while you're here. But if you knew where you belonged, then you'd be there, and then maybe you'd be in danger."

"I never looked at it that way," Ziggy admitted, accepting more brew from Daniel Nicholas's wife. "But sooner or later, I'll have to leave Voodoo Caye. And if I don't know my enemy, then he can walk right up to me. I won't know who he is."

"Why do you have to leave?" Peter demanded. "You got everything you need right here. You got friends here now. You got ideas for work—making a little hotel, bringing in some tourists. And you got a fine woman here, too."

"Really? Yesterday that fine woman was acting like she'd like to tear out my liver," Ziggy said dryly.

"Sure. That's how you know a woman loves you. They never get that mad at men they don't care about. You know?"

Ziggy was skeptical. He didn't think Cherish's anger had been inspired by anything personal. After all, he'd gone out of his way all week to make sure she had no reason to be personally annoyed at him. But did she get this angry at everyone who "interfered" with the Garifuna? He wondered if—

"Maybe the Doc is tired of being patient, huh? Tired of going to bed alone while you play cards with me or help Granny dry her herbs," Peter suggested.

Ziggy shook his head. "I doubt it, Peter. I think the Doc would bite me if I touched her tonight."

"Bite you? And would that be so bad?"

Ziggy chuckled. Then Granny Martinez came over and ended the conversation by leading him away. Now that darkness was falling, they were apparently approaching the climax of the *dugu,* and he was evidently going to be the guest star.

Granny made him drink a cup of some warm, bittersweet concoction. She didn't name its contents, but when it interacted with the alcohol he'd already drunk, the effect it had on his mind made him cease to care about such details, though he vaguely realized that she'd slipped him some kind of hallucinogen.

Someone made a bonfire, and then many torches were lit. At least a dozen of them were used in the dancing, which now grew frenzied and violent, in time to the wild beating of the drums. Chanting, Granny took his hand and led him forward into the circle of dancers. He shook his head, trying to clear it, but that only made the world spin wildly around him.

Granny ceased her chanting and started talking to him. His mind was growing too fuzzy to follow every word—what had he drunk?—but he managed to get the general idea. The spirits were all around them now, enlivened, stirred up, listening and speaking. Granny would help him cast out his demons and recall his own spirit. She asked him if he was ready.

Ziggy nodded, finding it difficult to make his body respond. He felt as if he were floating, even though he knew he was sitting. But when had he sat down?

Granny started chanting again, leading a chorus of fifty or sixty singers, all of them focusing on him. He wished he could understand, for they seemed to be saying something important. He blinked sleepily, finding it hard to keep his eyes open. He wondered when the dancers had become strange, writhing many-headed beasts of psychedelic color, like the spirits Granny had promised would visit him. He tried to ask her about this, but his tongue wouldn't obey him.

No wonder he'd never done any drugs, he thought fuzzily. This wasn't any fun. No. Fun was mastering a fast horse or car, flirting with a pretty woman and making love to her well, teasing the stuffed shirts in the family business and then surprising them with his abilities. Fun was annoying Catherine and trying to ruffle her feathers. Fun was following grandfather on one of his outrageous adventures, and then trying to outdo the old man—as if anyone could. Fun was...Cherish. Anything to do with Cherish. Fun was the redhead who filled his fantasies.

But where was she? Why was she leaving him alone with these grinning, dancing demons, this chanting high priestess and the cyclone of visions filling his head? She was usually so protective of him. Cleaning his wounds, making sure he ate, checking on him every night. But not last night. And he had needed her so badly last night.

Where were you? Where were you? he asked, but he made no sound. *Where are you now? Come to me, run to me.*

"Cherish!" someone called. "Cherish!"

She was there, then, though he didn't know whether she had appeared suddenly or taken shape over the eons, for he had no sense of time. A blaze of red hair, thick, lustrous, begging to be stroked. Eyes as green as that jade good-luck charm he'd bought in Hong Kong. Skin as soft as his best silk shirt, the one he'd lost in a poker game to that fat senator from down South who'd never be able to wear it.

Cherish, Cherish.

"I'm here, Ziggy. Are you all right?"

He felt her hand grope for his. He seized it roughly. She gasped. Had something frightened her? Did she see the demons, too? He tried to reassure her. Dancing demons were nothing. He'd protect her. He longed to shield her, to win her, to cherish her.

Granny spoke again, interrupting his thoughts, questioning him. The woman was powerful. There was no ig-

noring her, no escaping her demands. She led him down
a long, dark path, through a cave, beneath the sea and
beyond the dark side of the moon. She led him, last of
all, to the place he most wanted to avoid, to the dark
corners of his own mind.

Rain. Was it raining? His face was dripping wet. Cold.
He was cold. And the ground had gone from a gentle
swaying to a horrible, violent heaving. He tightened his
grip on the hand he held.

"They'll kill me now," he said.

"Who will kill you now?"

I just heard them decide to kill me. Got to get away.

"Who will kill you now?"

"Granny, don't make him remember this."

*A woman's voice. She sounded afraid, too. But he saw
no woman. No, he was alone, all alone. No one even
knew he was here, about to be killed. No one would ever
know where to look for his body.*

"Where are you?" a woman asked. A different
woman. The woman who had led him here, to a scene he
never wanted to see again.

"The boat," he whispered.

"Who—"

"Shh. They're coming back."

*He'd worked one wrist free of the ropes, but the other
was still tied tight. Why'd they have to come back so
soon? Didn't they want to eat or sleep or something before they murdered him? Humphrey Bogart and Errol
Flynn never got murdered this fast.*

"They can't hear you," the woman said. "Can you tell
me what's happening?"

"Argh!" Someone screamed. A man.

"Ziggy!"

*There was blood. His. A knife. His shoulder. Oh, God
it hurt! He blocked the next blow with his free arm.*

"Ziggy, stop!"

*A flash of blade, a slash down the side of his face. He
kicked hard. Somehow he got the knife and cut his other
wrist free, ignoring how sore it was from the rope burns.
He lashed out again, hearing more footsteps approaching. Someone seized his arm, and his heart flooded with
fear.*

Cherish bathed Ziggy's sweat-soaked chest with a cool
cloth. As she wrung it out, she observed that her hands
were still shaking. He stirred restlessly, muttering and
reaching for something. She soothed him, then turned
away, trying to stifle her tears.

The privilege of observing such exclusive rituals had
lost its thrill for Cherish when Ziggy had started to sweat
with terror and tremble violently, caught in a whirlwind
of violence and danger that only he could see. Ziggy was
very well liked by all the villagers, but none of them had
reacted as Cherish did to his ordeal during the *dugu*. She
had grown so horrified she had interfered in the ceremony and made some of the men carry Ziggy away from
the dancing and drumming and chanting.

She realized now why the Garifuna usually permitted
no observers at a *dugu*. They truly believed in the pow-
ers of *obeah* magic, as they believed in Granny, their
buye. They had no doubt that Granny was helping Ziggy,
and that he would be better for this experience. Cherish
had shocked them just as much as she would have
shocked any congregation of Catholics by hysterically
forcing the priest to stop in the middle of the Eucharist.

Academic, impartial observance of the *dugu* had been
all very well and good, until Cherish's faith in the cere-

mony had been tested. It had never occurred to her that the *dugu* would be such an ordeal for Ziggy. And she hadn't realized that seeing him suffer so would hurt more than losing her right arm. Her throat ached, her chest was on fire and she felt light-headed. How could she have exposed him to the *dugu*, knowing how desperately his mind had rejected whatever had happened to him the night of the storm?

She realized with shame that, in her intellectual arrogance, she hadn't really believed Granny's rituals would be so effective. Cherish had regarded them as a fascinating cultural tradition and had foolishly overlooked the fact that if a woman like Granny believed in the ceremony, then it must be truly powerful.

Ziggy was right, Cherish thought with a newfound humility. She could be so blind. She had lived too long in her ivory tower.

"Oh, Ziggy," she murmured, brushing damp tendrils of chestnut hair off his forehead. It seemed she had been on an emotional roller coaster ever since his arrival, and now she had just taken a terrible nosedive. She had failed them all tonight—Granny, the Garifuna, Grimly and Ziggy. And she had failed herself, too. She had spent so much energy setting herself apart, focusing on her intellect, and disdaining the most basic elements of the human condition—the need for affection and intimacy— that she had, to her mortal shame, become condescending.

"Doc, how's your face?" Granny asked, bustling into the little back bedroom of her cottage, where she had suggested Ziggy be taken until he regained consciousness.

Cherish lightly touched the soreness along her cheek, wondering how bad it looked. During the violent fit that had seized him, Ziggy had lashed out blindly and struck her hard enough to knock her down. "It's okay, Granny."

"Maybe we should put something cold on it," Granny mused, taking Cherish's·chin in her hand. She drew Cherish closer to the room's single lantern and studied the injury with professional interest.

"Granny, I'm so sorry I stopped the ceremony." Cherish blurted out the words. "It was wrong of me. I'm so ashamed. But he was so... I didn't know he would suffer like that. I couldn't...I didn't—"

"I think I know what you want to say, Doc," Granny said calmly. "You didn't know what would happen."

"No. And he...he's...I—"

"Yes, I can see that."

"I'm sorry," Cherish repeated miserably.

Granny smiled wisely and patted Cherish on the back. "Don't worry, Doc. Everyone knows you were only trying to protect him. It's too bad, though. He was very close to the spirits for a few moments."

"Do you think his memory has returned now?"

Granny shrugged. "We'll know when he awakens." Ziggy stirred in his sleep, but Granny restrained Cherish when she tried to return to his side. "Come outside for a bit, Doc," she urged. "Folks want to know how Ziggy is."

"I can't."

"The sooner you face everyone, the sooner you'll get over what happened tonight."

Realizing Granny was right, Cherish nodded. "But will he be all right alone?"

"Sure. We'll only leave him for a few minutes."

In the end, Cherish was glad she agreed to Granny's suggestion. The *dugu* was continuing without her and

Ziggy, but the villagers who broke away from the dancing, singing, praying and feasting long enough to ask her about Ziggy showed no hostility toward Cherish, despite her having broken up such an important religious ceremony. On the contrary, they seemed more concerned about her than about him. Well, they had expected Ziggy to have to undergo an ordeal, she realized, but no one had expected *her* to go to pieces. It was gratifying to know that, however much she was castigating herself, the Garifuna had already forgiven her.

Feeling unworthy but grateful for their tolerance, she returned alone to Granny's cottage. The beat of the drums and the ritual chanting filled its interior, making her shiver involuntarily as she opened the door to Ziggy's room.

It was empty. He was gone.

Eight

——

Eerie, monotonous chanting and the sinister beat of jungle drums roused him from a deep sleep. He opened his eyes to find himself alone in a strange, dim room. Where was Cherish? What was he doing here? What was that noise?

Sudden, vivid memories of the *dugu* flooded his mind as the chanting grew louder, filling his senses. He rose from the bed and pressed his fists against his temples as a fierce pain throbbed in his skull, a heavy pounding that joined the rhythm of the drums. The aromatic scent of the ceremonial fires, the strange ecstatic cries of the participants contacting the spirit world, and the shadows dancing all around him drove him mindlessly from this room, out of the cottage and away from the village.

He felt an almost supernatural strength in his limbs as he tore through the jungle, ignoring the vines that grabbed at his bare feet and the branches that whipped him in the face. But whatever he was running from was every bit as fast as he was, and it remained beside him, within him and all around him. The rational portion of his mind wanted to stop, to gasp for air, to quit this insane sprint through the dark jungle. But something stronger and more primitive drove him onward, into the heart of the night.

Luke Martinez was right: the air on Voodoo Caye was lush with spirits. The boy had told Ziggy all about the creatures that haunted this magical coast. Any moment Ziggy expected to run straight into the *Sisimito,* the gigantic hairy beast that tore men to pieces and carried off their women. He was sure he heard the chattering of *duendes* all around him, those strange, four-fingered dwarves who had been depicted by the Mayans in their stone carvings more than a thousand years ago. It was said that Dog-Dog's missing leg had been eaten by *duendes,* for Peter Sacqui had found their deep point-heeled footprints in the jungle the morning after Dog-Dog had crawled out of the bush, maimed and half dead.

Disoriented and dazed, Ziggy plunged through a grove of coconut palms and suddenly emerged, to his surprise, at the edge of Indigo Beach. He seemed destined to keep returning to this spot until he could remember how he had come here in the first place.

He finally stopped running and, breathing hard, leaned against a tree trunk and closed his eyes.

He must be going crazy.

Drawing deep breaths and trying to calm down, he gingerly rotated his bad shoulder. Granny had removed the stitches and told him it was healing well, but it sure wasn't up to a stunt like this. He opened his eyes and shook his head. *Duendes* and the *Sisimito?* What was the matter with him?

He hoped he was simply suffering the effects of whatever drug Granny had given him. He didn't want to believe he was completely losing his already tenuous grip on reality.

Exhausted and bewildered, he slid down to the base of the palm tree and sat with his back against it, looking out across the expanse of white beach to the vast ocean beyond. The rhythm of the waves was soft and regular tonight, so unlike that other night, the one that haunted him relentlessly, but whose details remained just out of his reach. He listened to the ebb and flow of the water, the soothing sound of nature at her most benevolent, and let his head drop back to rest against the tree trunk.

The sky overhead was a spectacle of celestial beauty. A full, pristine moon glowed so brightly against her dark setting that she almost seemed to pulse with life, and the stars twinkled in response to her subtle flirtation. Those heavenly bodies looked alive tonight, as did the plump, lacy clouds that drifted lazily by, their edges tinted to a glowing silver as the light of the moon caressed their shapes.

The view of that splendid sky stirred something deep inside Ziggy. The steady, rhythmic lapping of the foaming waves suggested another outlet for the urgent burst of energy that had sent him plunging through the jungle. No sooner had the thought come to him, than he heard her voice calling to him in the night.

"Where are you?" she cried, her voice drifting through the dense vegetation to pierce his heart.

For one mad moment he thought she was the *Ixtabay*, that Circe of the Belizean jungle who could most often be spotted sitting in a tree combing her hair. When she descended to walk above the surface of the ground, she could hypnotize a man and lure him deeper into the bush.

No one knew what she did with her lovers, for they went insane and died.

"Please, don't hide," she called, her voice more alluring than anything he had ever known.

Trembling, he rose to his feet, feeling the ocean breeze ruffle his hair. He didn't care about the consequences. Whatever the cost, he would go to her. He was sure he was half insane already, so let her do with him what she would. He knew what he wanted, and on this crazy moonlit night, with nothing at his back but the sea that had first brought him to her, he answered her call.

Instinctively guessing that Ziggy must have gone to Indigo Beach, that spot that drew him back more and more often, Cherish followed the footpath away from the village. She heard birds and monkeys screeching in the jungle and realized that something had disturbed them. What if Ziggy had strayed from the path and lost his way in the bush? Growing desperately worried, she started calling out to him as she approached the beach.

Finally, just when she had started to fear the drug from the *dugu* still had him in its grip, he answered her.

"Cherish?"

"Ziggy!" She practically shrieked his name, running straight into the grove of coconut palms off to her right. She was so close to the beach she could hear the lazy, insistent pulsing of the waves. She stumbled across a bed of silky green leaves with tiny pink-and-white flowers, and then Ziggy emerged from the other side of a clump of kapok trees.

She gasped in momentary fear, for with the light of the moon behind him, he looked menacing and formidably tall, his brown hair glowing with a celestial halo and his face hidden in shadows. He stalked forward with long strides, and she remembered Granny's warnings that lustful, half-human spirits prowled the jungle, waiting to pounce upon unwary maidens.

But when his arms closed around her, unyielding in their strength and urgent in their demand, she knew without a doubt who he was. His lips came down upon hers, and the taste of his warm mouth was too familiar to be mistaken. The musky smell of his body, the scent of her own soap on his skin and the hard, broad chest against hers flooded her senses. His kiss was hard and ruthless, lacking his usual finesse. She staggered under the force of his embrace and clutched the worn fabric of his borrowed red T-shirt. She grew dizzy and wondered wildly if she would faint before he stopped.

When he finally lifted his head to look down into her face, she drew in heavy, uneven gulps of air, staring back at him with wide, astonished eyes. It never occurred to her to speak, to protest, to resist him. She had finally entered the jungle, as he had wanted her to all along. There was no turning back now.

"I won't hurt you." His voice was rough. "I can't promise you anything else, but I won't hurt you."

"Ziggy." She slid her hands up to his face and drew his head down for another kiss. He was here and alive, and she was so tired of trying to be rational about her feelings for him. She wanted him more than she wanted to live another day.

He pressed her down into the lush vegetation at their feet, and it suddenly seemed so right that, after a lifetime of rigid standards, common sense and vigilant self-protection, she had chosen to abandon herself to a man with no name, no past and possibly no future. She wanted to mate like an animal, here in the jungle, with no words between them, no thought of tomorrow and no care for the consequences. Of every man she'd ever known, only he could make her feel this way, only he could give her this night, and she'd be worse than a fool to let him go.

His kisses were hot and desperate, his tongue restless and sweet. Their mouths met again and again, melding moistly, tasting and exploring with hungry insistence. He was demanding, commanding, overwhelming, draining her breath and strength away with the crushing embrace of his muscular arms and the soul-shattering power of his kisses. She struggled with the hem of his T-shirt, trying to pull it over his head, though their bodies were locked together and her vision swam with her own breathlessness. She succeeded at last and lay panting beneath him as he tossed it aside, so far into the darkness she doubted they'd find it again.

His mouth came down wetly upon hers again, and she answered him, thrusting her tongue against his as she moved her palms up and down the length of his back. His skin was wonderfully smooth and warm, and the bunch and flow of his sinewy muscles as he moved against her was thrilling. She had never known such pleasure in touching a man's body, had never experienced this heady mingling of pride, lust, admiration and awe at a man's strength and physical beauty. She wanted to touch all of him, to see whatever the shadows would permit, so she started tearing at the waistband of his shorts, desperate to free him from them.

His hands moved to the fabric of her sensible khaki blouse. disdaining the buttons, he tore the blouse open with one sudden, violent tug. She gasped and froze for a moment, then arched her back away from the ground so he could pull the garment off her shoulders and arms.

Ziggy rose to his knees and pulled Cherish up with him. He'd unfastened the clip that usually held her hair off her face, and now it tumbled around her shoulders in luxuriant red tresses, which glowed like embers beneath the pale moon. He kissed her again, tasting her, reveling in her response. He would never get enough of her. She had bewitched him, and he didn't even want to be set free. She could keep him prisoner in this jungle forever, as far as he was concerned. As long as he could have her, this way, whenever he wanted, as often as he wanted, forever and ever.

"Cherish," he murmured, tracing adoring kisses along her long, elegant neck. Her skin was as white and perfect as the most flawless marble, dusted here and there with a few sun-kissed freckles. He ran his palms down her smooth arms, gently squeezing the delicate shapes of her firm muscles, lightly tracing the fine bones of her wrists and hands. He kissed her again, then slid his arms around her to unfasten the clasp of her bra.

With a dreamy smile, she shrugged the straps over her shoulders, and he pulled the garment away from her body, taking the time to admire her full, heavy breasts with his eyes before he touched them.

Cherish closed her eyes and arched involuntarily toward him when he cupped her breasts in his palms and gently tested their weight. She braced her hands on his shoulders, unable to stop touching him, marveling at the way his muscles flexed subtly with every gentle movement of his hands. He brushed his knuckles along the sides of her breasts, making her quiver, then traced the dark circles of her areolae until her nipples ached painfully. He stroked them with his palms then, soothing her when she groaned and writhed, then teasing her with his fingers again while his mouth moved hotly against hers.

He lowered his head to taste the skin of her throat and shoulders, and she knew there would be telltale marks there tomorrow. She didn't care. She wouldn't have cared if he branded her for life.

His mouth was gentle on her breasts at first, his kisses sweetly soft upon her sensitized skin. But when he drew one burgeoning nipple into his mouth, Cherish arched her back and dug her nails into his shoulders, and his gentleness fled. She knew she would ache there later because of what he was doing with his teeth and his tongue and his strong suckling, but nothing seemed important right now except this wild, untamable, ungovernable feeling between them. She wanted him to devour her, to absorb her into himself, to make her forget her own name, as he had forgotten his. She wanted this almost-pain, this pleasure so strong it made her sob against his rumpled hair. She had longed to be this mad and free and uninhibited with him.

Somehow, they managed to work each other's shorts down and pull them off, then they rolled naked together in the soft bed of greenery. Cherish gasped when she felt the cold metal of his wristwatch against the bare skin of her stomach. Instead of taking it off, he made her warm it between her thighs while his fingers teased the warm, damp cleft there and his mouth continued to rove freely over her breasts.

His body was a marvel to her, a territory of thrilling new discoveries. Though she had bathed him and tended his injuries, she had never before cupped and caressed the hard cheeks of his buttocks, tasted the salty warmth of the smooth skin over his belly, or teased his flat, copper nipples into rigid peaks. Though she had seen him naked and fully aroused once before, she had not previously taken the time to admire him as she did now.

His manhood was silky smooth and intimidatingly hard, so sensitive that it responded with impertinent boldness to her every touch, even to her very glance. He rolled onto his back and let her look and touch, let her explore him as his hands toyed with her hair, stroked her back or arm, slipped teasingly between her legs. She had never known anyone so comfortable with his own body, so at ease with his masculinity, so willing to let the moments happen one by one.

She loved the way he sighed when she touched him, was enthralled by the way he groaned when she teased him more boldly. Most of all, she loved the way he looked at her. Drowning in tenderness, she rose above him and, guided by his hands, slid down over him, feeling him sink inside her as he arched his back.

Ziggy watched her rise above him like a goddess, crowned by the moon overhead. She murmured softly to him, but whatever she said was lost in the sound of the waves coming home to the shore. He felt the welcoming, wet heat of her body sheathing him, and he shuddered against the drive to thrust hard. He didn't want this to be done so soon. He was thankful that, whatever else he had forgotten, he remembered how to give a woman pleasure. With his hands on her thighs, he silently began the ancient dance, finding the tempo she wanted, urging her to take it to the limit.

The jungle buzzed and chattered all around them, but it had ceased to be a sinister place of demons and danger. Now nature serenaded this perfect thing happening between them and shielded them from all the worldly concerns that had driven them into the jungle's tenebrous embrace.

She rode him with a flowing, gliding grace that made his heart pound heavily and his breath come hard. When she cried out with pleasure and sagged bonelessly against him, he held her tightly against his chest, stroking her soft hair, lost in the tenderness he felt.

They kissed sweetly at first, then more urgently as his body demanded satisfaction and her own responded willingly. Still joined, he rolled her onto her back and pressed her into the soft cushion of flowers and leaves. Her hair tumbled wildly around her face and shoulders, and her eyes glowed in the moonlight. She looked like some forest nymph he had caught and seduced; though, when she raised her head and kissed him, he couldn't have said *who* the seducer was anymore. Her legs wrapped around him, an echo of his dreams and fantasies, her satiny thighs grasping him, locking them together in an embrace he never wanted to escape.

Arms braced on either side of her head, hands tangled in her hair, he thrust deeply into her, reveling in her throaty moan, the welcoming heave of her hips, the pressure of her palms against his back. Their lips met again as he continued his thrusts, pushing hard, wanting all of her, steeling himself against letting go too soon. She climaxed again, writhing wildly beneath him, moaning over and over, clutching him to her as he drove into her with total abandon. He joined her in her soaring flight over the moon and beyond the stars, joined her in their journey into each other. Out of the hopeless tangle of his forgotten past, there was one thing he knew for certain as he shuddered uncontrollably and buried his face in her hair; he'd never been in love before.

He blinked his eyes open in surprise and found her sitting above him, still naked. "How'd you get all the way over there?" he asked sleepily, reaching for her.

She smiled and let him pull her down against his chest. Nuzzling the coarse hair there, she murmured, "You fell asleep."

"When?"

"Must be almost two hours ago."

"Hmm. Sorry. Terrible manners."

"You've had a hard day." She stroked his stomach idly, but the casual tone in her voice didn't deceive him when she asked, "Did the *dugu* make you remember anything?"

He sighed. "Something," he admitted. "But I'm not sure what it means."

"Will it bother you to talk about it?"

"Do you mean, will it send me tearing through the jungle like a lunatic again?"

"No. Actually I mean will it give you one of those awful headaches or...spoil the mood?"

He kissed her forehead and lazily spread her hair across his shoulder. "It'll definitely spoil the mood. I've never felt so good in my whole life. As far as I know, I mean."

He felt her smile again. "I wish—"

"What?"

"I don't know." She shivered.

"Are you getting cold?"

"Yes, a little. Want to go home?"

"Home?" He liked how naturally she said it to him. "Yeah."

They rose a little stiffly to their feet, then searched for their clothes. They found enough for decency's sake, though Ziggy's T-shirt and Cherish's bra were apparently lost for good.

"Don't look under bushes like that, Ziggy. There might be poisonous snakes or something," Cherish advised, tying together the ends of her ruined blouse.

"You should have thought of that before you seduced me in the middle of a jungle," he chided, backing away from an unidentified sound beneath one bush.

"How remiss of me," she said dryly.

"Well, as long as you promise it'll happen again." He took her hand and led her toward the footpath. It was only when he caught a good look at her that he noticed the slight bruise starting to darken on her cheek. "What happened to you?"

"What? Oh, my face." She touched her cheek. "You hit me."

"I *what?*"

"You didn't mean to."

He tried to recall everything they'd done together tonight. He'd *hit* her? "When did I—"

"During the *dugu.*"

"During the—I *hit* you?"

"You were in some kind of trance. You never even saw me."

"Does it hurt?"

"Only a little."

"Good God." He cupped her cheek as gently as he could. "I'm sorry."

"No, *I'm* sorry I talked you into it. I never should have."

"You didn't know."

"Well, no, I didn't. But that's no excuse."

"Forget it, Cherish. Things like this happen when you live in another culture. You've got to learn to take things as they come."

"I don't know, Ziggy. I still wish—"

"Look, you got me involved in that ritual, and I slugged you for your trouble." He hesitated. "Are you all right?"

"Of course I'm all right."

"And so am I. So we're even. Okay?"

She smiled wryly. "I think I've just been talked into a corner, but okay."

"Let's go, then."

They were silent on the walk home, feeling no need for words, no need for anything but each other's company. The village was quiet at last, most people having fallen asleep after large quantities of food and drink, not to mention nonstop dancing. A few die-hards continued the revels, but the noise of the *dugu* was no more than a mild hum in the distance when Cherish and Ziggy entered their cabin.

He tugged on her hand when she turned toward the bedroom. "Not that bed. No way." When she looked at him questioningly, he added, "Unless you were planning to sleep alone?"

"No, but...the hammock?" She looked extremely doubtful.

He smiled. "Come on. It's better than that bed."

It took them a little time to get comfortable, but Ziggy proved to be right. They fell asleep locked in each other's arms, lulled by the gentle rocking motion of the old fish nets.

Ziggy was alone when he woke up, squinting against the sunlight. A quick glance at the wind-up clock in the kitchen revealed that it was nearly noon. Whatever he had imbibed at the *dugu* had left him with a hell of a morning-after feeling. Not a hangover exactly; more like a depth perception problem combined with slow mental responses. That was probably why it took him five minutes to notice the note Cherish had left on the table for him.

Didn't want to wake you. Peter Sacqui came by early to take me over to Rum Point. Granny says to join her for lunch. See you tonight.

He smiled and read the note two more times, as though it were a love letter. Well, coming from Cherish, it practically was. The doc wasn't exactly the gushy, sentimental type.

He half wished she had taken him to the mainland with her this morning. Not that she was likely to overlook anything important when she talked to the embassy—not Cherish—but he was sick of all this inactivity. Besides, he missed her already, and she'd probably be gone for another six hours.

However, his adventures last night had left his shoulder aching and his head throbbing, and he supposed he'd have only been miserable on a long trip in Peter's little boat. In fact, just the thought of being out on the water again made him feel queasy.

Despite his mental and physical ills, he was aware of a sweet, drained lassitude throughout his body; it had nothing to do with the *dugu* and everything to do with the woman who had slept in his arms last night. He could still feel the shape of her molded against him, their bodies conforming so perfectly to each other, her plump breasts pressed against his ribs and her thigh resting casually between his. He remembered the way she had nestled her head between his neck and shoulder, the way she had wrapped an arm around his waist. Was it any wonder that he'd had sweet dreams for a change?

However, despite the inner glow that countered his aching shoulder and muzzy head, he was aware that they had a lot of things to discuss when she got back.

First on the list was the fact that they hadn't used a condom or anything last night. And, during the ten or twelve days they'd been living on top of each other, he'd never noticed a packet of birth control pills lying around. They'd both been out of their heads last night—him especially.

And, quite apart from the possible question of pregnancy, he was uncomfortably aware that his sexual past was a mystery. He didn't know where he'd been or whether he'd had the good sense to take precautions with his previous sexual partners. He sure as hell hoped so. If not...

"Dammit."

Besides all that, he had to find out whether or not there was a particular women in his life. After last night, Cherish deserved to know, and he couldn't stand not being able to tell her with any certainly that she was his only lover. But if there *was* someone...

Who was he? Did he have anything to offer Cherish—a job, a name, a reputation? Or was he another small-time criminal, like the owner of the *Lusty Wench?* What was that guy's name again? Something Irish.

"O'Grady? Yeah, Michael O'Grady." He said the name a few times, trying to find something familiar.

"Was I a passenger on the *Lusty Wench,* or a prisoner? Why did someone tie me up and stab me?" He closed his eyes, willfully calling back images from the *dugu.* Why had someone decided to kill him? How was the bunny involved? He could vaguely recall seizing it during his escape from the boat. What was its significance?

He shot to his feet and retrieved the hideous thing from the desk, where he had left it for safekeeping before the start of the ritual. However, no amount of concentration on its ghastly, grinning face could provide an answer to his questions.

But it did remind him of something else? Ziggy drew a deep breath, relaxed and let the memory wash over him.

It was pleasant. He was with an old man, a short, bearded guy who looked a bit like Ernest Hemingway. The two of them were looking at stuffed toys.

Ziggy breathed evenly and concentrated.

The old man had taken him to FAO Schwartz, which was like the Promised Land. It was his sixth birthday, and they were playing with everything in the store.

"Grandfather?" Ziggy said aloud, his voice breaking.

The old man was incorrigible, stuffing the little boy with sweets and candies, cheating at all the games on display and making lots of funny growling and squeaking noises to animate the lifeless, stuffed animals.

"Grrrrr!" The old man picked up a stuffed grizzly bear and made it bound toward Ziggy, growling with comic ferocity as it pounced on the boy. Ziggy dissolved into squeals of laughter, running away from the old man and the bear.

"Grandfather!"

Ziggy's eyes snapped open. He was breathing hard, torn between excitement over discovering such a clear memory and despair that he didn't remember the old man's name, didn't even know if he was still alive.

"Ziggy!"

He nearly jumped out of his skin.

"Ziggy," Luke said again, sticking his head through the open doorway. "Aren't you coming to lunch?"

"Huh? Oh. Yeah." He rose from his chair and looked distractedly around the room. On instinct, he seized the bunny and tucked it under his arm.

He *did* have a family somewhere. Had they gotten worried about him yet? Were they looking for him? He had to know, especially now that things had changed between him and Cherish. He couldn't just hang out aimlessly on Voodoo Caye forever, waiting for his memory to return. It might take years; it might never happen at all, since there was nothing familiar here.

Only where *was* there something familiar? New York? Paris? London? Yes, London. He could remember the wallpaper pattern inside a bedroom at the Ritz. Unfortunately he didn't know if he'd been a paying guest there, or a burglar.

"Ziggy, are you coming?" Luke asked impatiently.

Bunny in hand, Ziggy stalked wordlessly out the door, followed by the boy. On the way to Granny's, he was greeted by many of his new friends.

In truth, he had grown to like it here. It was tempting to consider forgetting about his previous life, to remain here with Cherish Love and the Garifuna and make a new life on Voodoo Caye. But, he acknowledged, the temptation wasn't only due to the pleasure of Cherish's company, the friendliness of the villagers and the beauty of the island. No, he was also afraid of what he might find out about himself if he left. There were too many appalling possibilities.

Besides he couldn't risk hurting Cherish. What if he was some kind of lowlife criminal and was wanted by the police? What if whoever wanted to kill him was still searching for him? Good God, what if his enemies came to Voodoo Caye? His presence here could put Cherish, not to mention all his Garifuna friends, in terrible danger.

Head and belly aching, he wondered desperately what he should do. He couldn't go on like this any longer. He *had* to find out who he was.

It was nearly sunset when Peter Sacqui docked his boat at the pier. Cherish scarcely acknowledged the greetings of the other fishermen as Peter helped her disembark. With a heavy heart, she plodded gracelessly through the village, wondering how she could face Ziggy with this news.

"Hey, Doc!" Alexa Nicholas, Daniel's wife, greeted her.

"Hi."

"We're talking about the restaurant we're gonna have when the tourists start coming to Voodoo Caye," Alexa explained cheerfully.

Cherish stopped in her tracks. "Ziggy suggested this, right?"

"Sure did," Alexa said, her gaze flickering momentarily to the marks Ziggy had left on Cherish's skin.

Cherish self-consciously pulled the collar of her blouse together. "I see. Where is he?" She avoided Alexa's knowing smile, feeling her cheeks grow hot.

"Ziggy's down at Indigo Beach, I think. Maybe we should build a dock down there, since the reef is in that direction. For the scuba divers, you know."

"Uh-huh," she answered grimly.

Telling Ziggy this news might not be so bad, after all. He was having a detrimental effect on all of them. The Garifuna wanted to turn Voodoo Caye into Miami Beach, and *she* had had sex with a virtual stranger without using any protection whatsoever. She must have been out of her mind last night. And it was all Ziggy's fault.

Yes, telling him what she had learned wouldn't hurt nearly as much as she'd thought it would. This morning, she'd awakened in his arms with the feeling that her life was only just beginning. But now, after her phone call to the American Embassy, she wished she'd never laid eyes on the man.

She should have seen this coming. It's not as if there hadn't been plenty of clues. But no, she had blundered ahead, and now she would pay for it.

She found him at the beach, as expected, sitting at the water's edge with a troubled expression on his face.

"Ziggy."

He turned around. "You're back!" He rose to his feet and came over to kiss her.

She backed away.

A strange expression crossed his face. "What's wrong? What did you learn from the embassy?"

"Your wife has turned up." Her voice was flat. "Catherine is waiting for you at the American Embassy in Belize City."

Nine

When they arrived at Rum Point the following morning, where Peter Sacqui had taken them in his boat, they sought out the tiny bus station. Though the sea was calm today, the trip had left Ziggy with a heaving stomach and tightly wound nerves. Being on a boat again was like being caught in the middle of his nightmares, and it had taken every ounce of his self-control not to give in to his terror and cower on the deck like a seasick child.

That effort, combined with his sleepless night, had left him exhausted and short-tempered. Cherish, who had barely spoken to him since her startling announcement on the beach yesterday, now aggravated him further by examining the bus designated for Belize City as if it were a horse she intended to buy.

"Can we just get on board and find a damn seat?" he asked.

"We've got to make sure it's safe," she insisted, crouching down to examine one of the tires. "I've traveled in Central America, and you haven't. I mean, you don't know if..." She cleared her throat and continued. "If there are visible threads on the tires, that means a blowout could occur, and it's a long drive to Belize City."

"No threads. See? Can we find a seat now?"

"I've got to check the others. If three or more of the tires are bald, then we risk a bus plunge. And it's pretty hilly in the interior."

"We're not going into the interior," he snapped. "Belize City is on the coast. *We're* on the coast. Why would we go—"

"There's no major direct road from here to Belize City. We've got to take the Hummingbird Highway into the mountains to get to the Western Highway, which goes back out—"

"Oh, God." He lowered his head. "I can see it's going to be a long day."

"Driver," Cherish called, stopping the uniformed man who was climbing aboard the bus. "Could you check the brakes before we leave?"

The chubby man frowned at her. "Why?"

"To make sure they work, of course."

"Look," he said. "The bus is stopped, isn't it, miss? See? The brakes, they work fine." He boarded the bus.

"But I—"

"Cherish, forget it. Let's just live dangerously for a change," Ziggy suggested tiredly.

"I lived dangerously two nights ago, and where did that get me?"

Since he had no answer to that, he waited quietly until she had finished her inspection of the bus. Then they got on board, making their way past three dozen passengers, as well as a baby pig and four chickens.

After the bus had pulled away from Rum Point and was rolling along the potted road heading north, Ziggy asked, "When do you think we'll get to Belize City?"

She shrugged. "Late. Not until after dinner."

"About a twelve-hour trip, then. Well, I suppose she'll wait," he said absently, thinking of the unknown wife he was to meet at the end of this journey. "Look, Cherish, don't you think we should talk?"

"Talk?"

"Yes. We need to talk about this."

"About what?"

"Don't push me," he warned through gritted teeth. "I'm not in the mood for one of those female conversations."

"What 'female conversations?' " she demanded.

"You know." He sighed. "The way women fight."

"What way?"

"What way? Okay, I'll tell you what way." He turned toward her. "I ask what's wrong. You say nothing's wrong. But because you say it in a tone that could freeze water, I ask again. You answer the same way. Then you give me a look that could scorch earth and I ask again. Then you say that I don't want to know what's wrong. Then I say that I *do* want to know. Then you say that I really don't. Then I say, 'Yes, I do. I really do. What's wrong?' And you say, 'Never mind. You wouldn't understand.' "

"I never do that! I *never* act that way."

"Then shouldn't we talk about our situation?"

"What situation?" she asked in a voice that could freeze water.

He looked as if he'd like to strangle her. "We slept together two nights ago. Without any protection."

"Keep your voice down."

Raising his voice, he continued. "And now you're delivering me into the arms of a wife I can't even remember."

"Fine," she said. "We've discussed our situation. Happy now?"

"No, I'm not happy! Are you happy? Is this what you thought would happen when you crawled into my hammock?"

"Why don't you say that a little louder, Ziggy? I think there's someone at the front of the bus who didn't quite hear you," she snapped.

"What are we going to do about this? What if you're pregnant right now? What if I gave you, uh, something *besides* a baby?"

"What a charming suggestion."

"Dammit, I'm trying to act like an adult about this! *I* didn't expect you to come home and tell me I was married to someone else."

"Someone whose name is written all over your twelve-thousand-dollar watch. Someone whose name you've remembered in your fever dreams. Someone who I should have *known* would be looking for you!"

His jaw dropped. "Look, Cherish, there's no point in being angry at yourself over this. You couldn't—"

"I'm not angry at myself!" She thumped her chest so hard he winced. "I'm angry at *you*. Why couldn't you be boorish and dull and smelly and stupid and homely and...and...?" She swallowed. "We're getting off the subject."

"We are?" He reached for her hand. She snatched it away. "Cherish, what are we going to do?"

"I'm going to turn you over to your wife, who's probably the person with whom you've spent all that time at Maxim's and the Ritz, and she's going to help you recover your memory completely."

"And you're going back to Voodoo Caye?"

"After I see Grimly, yes."

"No, Cherish! I'm not letting you."

"Oh, really? And what do you think your *wife* is going to have to say about that?"

"I haven't *got* a wife, dammit!" They stared at each other in shocked silence. Finally he said, "Hey! How about that? I remembered something."

She sighed. "This is just wishful thinking, Ziggy. Mr. Waterson at the embassy says a woman named Catherine has inquired after a missing brown-haired man of thirty-two. In answer to his questions, she says that, yes, he should be wearing *this* watch." She tapped his wrist. "And he answers to the 'pet name' of Ziggy. I hardly think that *two* such people could have disappeared off the Belizean coast this month."

"I don't care. I would know if I had a wife."

"You don't even know your own name!"

"But I'd remember a wife," he insisted stubbornly. "That night in the jungle, I knew I'd never . . . never . . ." He gave up. He might have told her more, told her how she'd made him feel, but her expression was about as friendly as a scorpion's. Anyhow, for all he knew, he had married without love. Feeling utterly despondent, he turned away from Cherish and stared out the window.

It was a long, uncomfortable trip across hot countryside and bumpy roads. The piglet wasn't housebroken, and the resultant odor nearly made Ziggy decide to walk the rest of the way to Belize City. The only reason he didn't suggest it was that *he* wasn't going to be the first one to break the frigid silence between himself and Cherish. It wasn't his fault that he'd lost his memory, and he refused to be blamed for a wife he didn't know he had. So he sat silently, with his bunny on his lap, and watched Belizean jungles and villages pass by.

About halfway through the trip, the bus made a rest stop at an isolated rural coffeehouse. A small child tried to take away Ziggy's bunny. He took it back, and when the child started crying, he said absently to Cherish, "I left all my poker winnings with Granny. Give this kid five bucks, will you?"

She looked appalled. "I can't do that! I can't alter his cultural perspective like that! Do you want him to ask for a handout from every tourist he sees for the rest of his life?"

"See that farmer over there with the double-barreled shotgun? That's his father. Give the kid five bucks, or you'll have to explain to my *wife* why I didn't survive the trip."

"Oh, my God." She gave the kid five bucks. Back on board the bus, she demanded, "Why does trouble follow you wherever you go? All of Belize will be contaminated by the time you're through!"

"I think that's a slight—"

"How could you encourage Alexa Nicholas to open a restaurant for the tourist trade?" she raged.

"Oh, we're back to my pollution of Garifuna society again, are we?"

"Don't be snide."

"Then don't be such a pigheaded, pompous snob," he snarled back. She gasped at the insult. He sighed. "Okay, sorry. I'm sorry. But you are so blind where they're concerned, it makes me want to shake you."

"What do you mean blind? I've read everything ever written about them. I've studied their customs in person for over six months. No one—"

"What about looking at them as ordinary people struggling with life in the twentieth century, Cherish?"

"Naturally their traditional ways are threatened—"

"Oh, for God's sake! Do you really expect them to live in a vacuum? People don't change just because they're *threatened*. They change because that's the way of things. That's why our ancestors left their caves and built houses and invented furniture."

"The Garifuna should be permitted to change on their own," Cherish insisted. "The interference of the white man, or the developed world, or whatever you want to call it, has never benefited any tribal or aboriginal culture with which we have come in contact. You have only to look at the overpopulation and widespread famine in Africa, or the conditions of the Mayans here in Central America, or—"

"Right or wrong, like it or not," he said, interrupting her, "the reality is that the population of Voodoo Caye is less than half of what it was ten years ago. Everyone has gone to the mainland to find jobs, further their education, or meet more members of the opposite sex. None of Daniel and Alexa's grown children have remained on the island, Cherish. Have you talked to these people about anything besides old customs and rituals?"

"Of course I—"

"Then you ought to realize how many of them tell that same story. Their children want to leave or have already left. If Voodoo Caye remains the way it is, in another generation there won't be any young people left on the island. Then who will carry on the traditions you're so concerned about preserving? What will happen to their culture when their families are scattered like dandelion seeds?''

Feeling a weight of guilt in her chest, for she truly hadn't thought about these things, despite her professed friendship with the islanders, she said, "So you think developing tourism on the island will encourage the young people to remain?''

"Yes, I do.'' He shrugged. "It's not that they don't love Voodoo Caye or their families. But they feel that there's no future for them on the island. It's not a question of whether or not they *should* want to live exactly like their fathers and grandfathers. The fact is, they've decided they don't want to. And if a boy doesn't want to be a fisherman, or if a girl wants to be something besides a fisherman's wife, then there's really nothing left for them on Voodoo Caye.''

Cherish looked past Ziggy and out the window. "I guess you've got a point, Ziggy.''

"I know there are a lot of negative aspects of opening up a small, communal society to outside influence. I've heard that some formerly peaceful communities along this coast now have trouble with theft, violence, drugs and begging. I don't want to see that happen on Voodoo Caye any more than you do, Cherish. But isolation and obscurity isn't the answer anymore. If development is carefully planned for the benefit of the community, it could be so much better for everyone there than what's happening now.''

"This is what you meant when you said I wanted what was best for me, not what's best for them." She met his gaze. "Isn't it?" He didn't have to answer. "I guess I was so wrapped up in..." She sighed and shrugged, feeling ashamed of herself.

"Well, I know you feel you've got a lot to prove." He covered her hand with his, relieved that she didn't pull away. "Wanting to prove yourself can block out everything else and make a person obsessed. Catherine's always been that way."

Her head snapped up. They stared at each other. Finally, with a sad smile, she pulled her hand away. "You see? You're starting to remember her."

"Catherine," he repeated, bewildered. Why was there no rush of longing, no desire for his beloved? When he thought of her name, he mostly felt a deep-seated, exasperated kind of affection. What was it about her that made him shake his head? "She's perfect," he said slowly.

"Excuse me?"

"When I think of Catherine..." He frowned, trying to find the right words. "I'm fond of her, but I don't actually like her very much. She's..." He nodded, sure he was on to something. "She's always so damn perfect. She knows everything. She does everything right. She's completely reliable, reasonable, intelligent, efficient." He started to grin. "Hey! You know, I think things *are* starting to come back to me!"

"That's good, Ziggy. And I'm sorry you don't like your wife better, but I don't think you should tell me any more."

"But I—"

"*Please* don't tell me any more." She turned away, but not before he saw the sparkle of tears in her eyes.

The journey finally ended, but not before the strained silence between them had become unendurable. Cherish hailed a cab outside the bus station in crowded, noisy, colorful Belize City and directed the driver to take them to the American Embassy. She paid the taxi when he let them off outside an elegant building set back from the road, behind locked gates.

Holding his bunny, Ziggy stared at the imposing edifice while Cherish gave their names to the guards out front. He knew a moment of panic when they were told they could go to the door.

"Cherish, I don't think—"

"Come on, Ziggy. She's been waiting all day," Cherish urged soothingly. She wouldn't give in to tears, not now. Despite everything, he needed her support, and that was what mattered most. There would be time enough later for tears. There would be plenty of nights when she would know he was sleeping in another woman's arms. Feeling her throat grow tight, she gave him a little shove forward. "It's okay, I'm right beside you."

He took her hand, hoping his own wasn't shaking. "Just stay by me, okay? I, uh, this is really..."

"You'll probably remember everything as soon as you see her," Cherish assured him. *And then you'll forget all about me and one wild night under the Voodoo moon.*

They climbed the steps to the front of the building and were admitted through the front door by another guard who used the intercom to tell Mr. Waterson that Dr. Love and her companion had arrived. Within moments, Mr. Waterson entered the reception area to greet Cherish and Ziggy.

"Dr. Love!" A tall, rangy man with a receding hairline, he shook her hand with excessive vigor. "We had begun to grow worried. But then, these bus services are so unreliable, so *laissez-faire,* so—"

"Uh, yes." Cherish interrupted him. "And this is Ziggy, Mr. Waterson." She saw the man's gaze flash immediately to the pink bunny in Ziggy's arms, and the stunned, disbelieving expression that crossed his face almost made her want to laugh. She observed that Ziggy had a death grip around the bunny's throat, so she decided they'd better not drag out the suspense. "If you don't mind, Mr. Waterson, Ziggy is naturally very anxious to meet . . ."

Her voice trailed off as a petite, red-haired woman came forward cautiously. Her silk dress must have cost half of Cherish's annual salary, but it was too showy for anything but an inaugural ball, and the color didn't suit her complexion at all. If *this* was Ziggy's "perfect" Catherine, then he must have been blinded by love. The woman proved to be as dramatic as her dress. After whispering Ziggy's name with heartfelt relief, she ran forward to fling herself violently against him. The performance was only marred by her double take upon seeing the bunny. Then she smothered him in a series of extravagant embraces.

Ziggy threw Cherish a look of total panic. It reminded her of the way he had looked that first night in her cabin, when he was out of his mind with fever and pain, and shocked to discover that he'd lost his memory. The expression broke her heart, for it was one she knew he didn't like anyone but her to see. She steeled herself not to grab this awful woman—who was now babbling about how glad she was to see her "darling" again—and remove her from Ziggy's presence.

"Darling! Say something!" the woman commanded eagerly.

"I, uh . . ." He glanced wildly at Cherish again. "How do you do?"

"Ziggy, dear, don't you know me? Darling, I'm your wife. Catherine."

"We're married?" he asked weakly.

"Of course we're married."

"You're sure about that?"

"You really don't remember?"

"Sorry, I . . . I think I . . . Cherish? Can you and I talk for a . . ." His breath grew fast and shallow, and he looked as if his head was starting to ache again.

His wife turned to face Cherish. To give Catherine credit, she didn't even look dismayed at the sight of the "really built" redhead with the "great jugs" with whom Ziggy had spent nearly two weeks. Cherish had expected Ziggy's wife to show some concern about his relationship with her—even perhaps some latent hostility. Instead, Catherine greeted Cherish politely and thanked her profusely for saving Ziggy's life. Cherish noticed that the woman wore quite a rock on the fourth finger of her left hand. It was hard to imagine Ziggy buying her something so vulgar.

"And now," Catherine said, "I think I'd like to be alone with my husband. We have so much catching up to do."

"Of course," Mr. Waterson said quickly. "We understand."

"If you don't mind," Cherish said, "I have just a few questions."

"Questions?" Mr. Waterson said. Cherish figured he was probably impatient to get home to his own wife. It was rather late, after all; the embassy was practically deserted. But this was important.

"Having become good friends with Ziggy during the past couple of weeks, there are some things I'd really like to know."

Catherine didn't miss a beat. "Of course."

"Things like, what's his full name? What was he doing on the *Lusty Wench?* How did he get knife wounds and rope burns? Where were—"

"Quite understandable," Mr. Waterson agreed, interrupting her. "But perhaps these questions could wait until tomorrow, Dr. Love? It's been a long day for all of us. Ziggy looks exhausted, as do you. And, frankly, I'm violating several rules by letting you into this embassy after hours. Besides, not to sound callous, but my wife has had dinner waiting at home since—"

"Yes, but—"

"It's all right, Cherish," Ziggy responded, looking at Catherine. "Why don't you go ahead? We can settle things tomorrow."

Startled by the change in his manner, she stood there stock-still for so long that Catherine finally prompted, "Dr. Love? Do you have someplace to stay tonight?"

"Yes. I'm staying at the Corridor Institute of Anthropological Studies."

"Voluntarily?" Mr. Waterson asked. When she looked at him quizzically, he commented, "It's just that Dr. Corridor has something of a reputation."

"I get along with him okay," Cherish said absently, turning her gaze upon Ziggy again. He was still looking at his wife. Cherish's heart ached painfully. Yes, as she had predicted, he was starting to remember. She was ashamed that she couldn't even feel glad for him. In a husky voice, she asked, "What time should I come back tomorrow, Mr. Waterson?"

"Around ten o'clock, shall we say?"

"Okay." Feeling awkward, she crossed the hallway to stand before Ziggy. "Will you be all right?"

His gray eyes met her gaze. She'd never seen them look more opaque. "Yeah, I guess so." He shrugged. "What can I say? Thanks for everything, Doc."

"You're welcome." She would not cry. She would *not* cry. She turned away.

"Cherish?"

"Yes?" She turned back. *Please give me a sign, even though I didn't have the guts to ask you for one.*

He held out the bunny. "It's not much," he said quietly, "but it's the only thing that's mine. I want you to have it."

"Oh, really, darling," Catherine chided, "don't be silly. After all Dr. Love has done for you, surely a more appropriate gift would—"

"No," Cherish insisted. "This is all I want. It'll remind me of..." She drew a deep breath and struggled to control the hot sting in her eyes. Knowing what it must have cost Ziggy to part with the mysterious, ugly, pink rabbit, she took it by the ear and said sincerely, "Thank you, Ziggy. I'll take good care of it."

Then she turned and left him with his wife.

Ten

One of the good things about Grimly Corridor was that Cherish never felt any obligation to be polite to him. She arrived unannounced on his doorstep at nine o'clock that night and told him she was staying for a day or two. She explained the situation briefly to him, ignoring his ranting and raving about all the working hours she was losing on account of Ziggy. Then she went up to her room to be alone.

Grimly's personal servant, a *mestizo* man named Juan who was as wide as he was tall, brought her something to eat about an hour later. Juan was the only person in the world who could put up with Grimly for any length of time, probably because he was just as mean and ornery as his boss. Cherish was afraid to admit to the acid-tongued, quick-tempered, sour-faced mountain of a man that she couldn't choke down even a bite of the beautiful dinner he had prepared for her, so she dumped most of it over the balcony.

The Corridor Institute was a colonial-style villa on the outskirts of Belize City. Since Grimly had alienated virtually every gardener in the entire district, the garden, which Cherish's balcony overlooked, had long since been overtaken by the jungle.

Exhausted and depressed, Cherish treated herself to a hot bath. Then, wearing only the sleeveless, white cotton nightgown she had packed for this trip, she picked up the stuffed bunny by its floppy ears and wandered out onto the balcony. Monkeys chattered in the jungle, and the mating cry of a lonesome macaw reached out to her.

The moon was full, as it had been on that magical night on Voodoo Caye, and she gazed longingly up at the glowing orb, remembering. The air was lush with the scent of orchids, frangipani and jasmine, and though she could not hear the ocean, she could smell it in the gentle, easterly breeze.

It had never occurred to her that Catherine was a redhead. Ziggy remembered a redhead from his past, but he had never associated her with Catherine. What had he said? Oh, yes. The redhead had been his first lover. Cherish shrugged and turned her face into the breeze, feeling it lift her own hair away from her face. Well, perhaps he had meant Catherine and just not known it.

Cherish frowned suddenly. No, that couldn't be right. Ziggy had surely lost his virginity years ago, and at that time, the woman he described had already been older than Cherish was now. Catherine looked about twenty-five.

She stroked the bunny's ears. It seemed strange that her red hair would remind Ziggy of a woman from years ago but never once remind him of his own wife.

His wife. The words rang through her mind and hurt beyond bearing. She had been so distraught upon finding out about Catherine yesterday that anger had been her only defense. But it truly wasn't his fault that he hadn't known about Catherine; and he'd made love to Cherish without knowing he had a prior commitment. If anyone was to blame for that night, it was her. She had insisted on the *dugu,* which tore at his mind and drove him into the jungle, and then she had taken advantage of his needs in order to fulfill her own.

Not that those hours with Ziggy now seemed like anything to associate with blame. They were all she had, all she would ever have of him, now that he had been reclaimed by his wife.

A tear rolled down her cheek.

She brushed it away and gritted her teeth against this appalling sentimentality. After the way she had behaved, Ziggy was probably glad to be rid of her. She hoped she would have the opportunity tomorrow to tell him she was sorry for having misjudged him so. His flippancy and frivolity concealed a serious, caring nature; in his own way, he had tried to help the Garifuna during the short time he had been on Voodoo Caye. She knew that everyone there would miss him terribly. Who would teach slang to the women, basketball to the children and obscure card games to the men? Who would help the islanders further their newfound dream of opening up Voodoo Caye to controlled tourism and giving their children a reason to stay on the island?

"Oh, Ziggy." She sighed, missing him terribly.

Who would hold her through the long, lonely nights? Would there ever be another man who'd make her want to throw aside all her inhibitions and behave as she had behaved with him? She could never again settle for the tepid kind of love affair she had experienced before meeting him, and she was afraid there would never again be another man who was persistent, clever, charming, sensitive and tolerant enough to get past all the road blocks she had put up. Would she ever want another man to try?

"I wish..."

She wished for what she couldn't have now. She had wasted her chance, and besides, he belonged to another woman. Overcome by desolation, she hugged the bunny tightly to her, letting her tears flow freely this time.

The bunny wasn't nearly as nice to hug as Ziggy. It wasn't even a comforting substitute. The thing didn't feel at all the way she had thought it would. It wasn't soft, like the stuffed animals of her girlhood. Its torso was hard, as if it were stuffed with sand or flour.

She tensed. *The bunny.* Why had it always been so important to Ziggy to keep the bunny safe? Why had he given it to her now?

Her sobs subsided as she forced herself to analytically examine the moment he'd given her the bunny. Had it been a gesture of gratitude and friendship? Or had it been another instinctive move to protect the bunny? His face had borne the expression he usually wore when another of his headaches was coming on. What—

A sharp sound in the darkness made her gasp and whirl around, her heart pounding with sudden fear. Someone was climbing the thick tangle of vines that crept up the side of the villa and led to her balcony! She was just about to scream when a head of thick, brown hair appeared and a familiar pair of gray eyes peered at her over the railing of the balcony.

"Thank God, I'm nearly there! This isn't half as easy as Errol Flynn always made it look."

"Ziggy!" She dropped the bunny and gaped at him, blinking away tears to get a better look at him.

Hauling himself over the railing, he paused, wincing at the pain in his bad shoulder and panting heavily. He glared at her and said, "By all means, don't give me a hand or anything like that."

"Ziggy!" She pulled him the rest of the way to safety. His arms came around her and his mouth came down upon hers with hungry insistence.

Her arms slid around his neck without conscious thought, and she returned his hot, intimate kiss with every ounce of her strength. Breathing heavily, he raised his head at last and traced the tracks of her tears with gentle fingers. "You've been crying," he murmured.

"What are you doing here?"

"Kiss me," he ordered. He melded his mouth to hers again, warm and moist, loving and demanding.

"But, Ziggy," she sputtered helplessly, quivering with excitement as his lips explored her eyelids, her cheekbones, the sensitive spot beneath her ear.

His hands were everywhere, caressing her back, stroking her hair, cradling her face, squeezing her firm buttocks, brushing the sides of her breasts. Her senses were flooded with him. His mouth tasted of strong coffee, his hair still smelled of her own floral shampoo, his skin was warm and vibrant, his fast breathing and incoherent murmurs were like an erotic symphony in her ears, and every intense flash of those gray eyes made her heartbeat accelerate.

"But where's Catherine?" she asked breathlessly.

He grimaced. "That awful woman? Let's not talk about her."

"But Ziggy—"

"Kiss me again."

Lost in the velvety heat of his tongue twining with hers, she clutched him when the world spun crazily, then realized he was lifting her and carrying her inside to the bed. "No! We can't!"

He braced one knee against the mattress and lowered her to the bed, following her down swiftly and imprisoning her with his weight. "Of course we can," he breathed against her skin, pulling her nightdress up over her legs.

She pushed feebly at his hands, gasping when she felt his fingers against the sensitive flesh of her inner thighs. "No, you're supposed to be at—"

His hard kiss stopped her words, and his hand slid under her nightgown to massage her abdomen, making her loins ache sweetly. "Touch me," he murmured.

Helpless to deny the drowsy desire in his voice, she caressed his face lovingly, meeting his kisses, nuzzling his soft hair. Encouraged by this, he pulled her nightgown further up.

"Please," she implored. "We can't just— Oh! Ohhh..."

She was lost after that, made mindless and conscienceless by the clever teasing of his fingers, the musky aroma of his arousal, the driving force of her love. Nothing on earth, no amount of willpower, no sense of integrity, could stand against the force of the gale sweeping through her soul. She felt she would rather die than make him stop now.

"I was afraid I'd never see you again," he said hoarsely, pressing his face into the giving softness of her belly, moving his hands restlessly over her smooth legs.

"I said I'd come back tomorrow." She stroked his nape and ran her fingers through the gleaming chestnut waves of his hair.

"No, I mean like this. Alone." He yanked the nightgown up and pressed his wet, open mouth against her stomach.

She sighed and rubbed her calf against his thigh, frowning at the abrasive feel of the hem of his shorts. "Take your clothes off," she whispered.

He undid the fastening at his waist and kicked off the khaki shorts she had given him, then pulled off his violently gaudy, hand-me-down, tropical shirt. They embraced then, aligning their bodies head to toe, pressing their foreheads together as they reveled in the wonder of being together. Linking his fingers with hers, he kissed her again, searching her mouth with his tongue, letting his lips tell her without words how much he needed her.

They rolled over together on the broad, firm mattress, flinging away the fluffy pillows and brushing aside the crisp, cotton sheets. Ziggy buried his face in her hair and inhaled deeply. Swamped by tenderness, she kissed the smooth column of his throat, the hard muscles of his arms and the pink scar on his shoulder. She kissed his wrists, where the burn marks had finally disappeared, and the long, healing scratch on the right side of his face, which would probably also leave a scar.

The heat of his lips burned through the fabric of her nightgown and made her gasp when they finally encountered the bare flesh of her abdomen and legs. He grasped her buttocks in his strong hands and lifted her slightly as he lowered his head to intimately kiss the hot, wet, aching place between her thighs. She tangled one hand in his hair while the other reached above her head to grasp the brass headboard, and her legs parted willingly as he eased his shoulders between them to better pursue his exploration of her body's most secret crevices.

She felt the rasp of his unshaven cheek against the tender flesh of her inner thigh and the pressure of his fingers digging into her bottom. The agile swirl and thrust of his tongue made her sob with pleasure, and the heat of his breath against her most sensitive flesh made her moan when he whispered shameless, erotic things to her.

Flushed and dazed, she begged, "Now. *Please*. I want you *now*. I can't... Oh, Ziggy."

He kissed the slender hands that tugged at him and submitted to her demands. He drew her grasping fingers to the hard, pulsing shaft between his thighs. "Show me what you want," he urged thickly, closing his hand around hers and shifting so that their hips met.

She didn't wait or hesitate or tease. Her heart was too desperate to permit her such indulgences. She led him to the aching void that waited for him, only for him, and cried out when he entered her.

"Yes." She rose to meet him, arching off the bed, pulling his hips down with her hands.

He thrust deep and hard, making the bed rock and the headboard rattle, and they sighed in mutual satisfaction when they felt their bodies joined as closely as possible.

"Don't be gentle," she whispered. "I want to feel you all day tomorrow. All week. The rest of my life."

He pulled back, then drove into her again. "Tell me you love me."

"I love you." She couldn't have held back the words even if she had wanted to. She felt the hot flick of his tongue across her lips as he plunged into her, and she arched against him in ecstatic response.

"Tell me again," he whispered, grinding his hips against hers, guaranteeing that she would indeed feel him for a long time afterward.

"I love you." She had always known he didn't play fair. Why bother to resist? "Oh, Ziggy, I love you."

The whirlwind came upon them, drawing cries of soul-deep delight from their throats and making them shudder helplessly in each other's arms. Lost in the storm, they clung together, rocked by the astonishing pleasure they shared.

They lay quietly in each other's arms for a while then, content to merely be together, not even willing to pull apart enough to let the soft tropical breeze cool their damp, overheated bodies. As her breathing returned to normal and her blood stopped thundering wildly through her veins, Cherish became aware of a thousand questions she should ask him, but she was reluctant to end the perfect peace of love's afterglow.

He turned his head slightly and buried his face in her hair, inhaling its scent. Then, at last, he said, "Aren't you going to ask me about my wife?"

"Only *you* could say something like that at a moment like this."

"You seemed so interested in talking about her when I got here," he said innocently.

She sighed. "All right. Tell me."

He shifted his position, rolling on his side so they faced each other. "She's not my wife. I was right. You should listen to me more often."

"Ziggy, she—"

"No! Listen to me, I know what I'm talking about. Whoever the real Catherine is, she's got flaxen hair and blue eyes, not red hair and brown eyes. I'm sure of it."

She sat up suddenly. "You're starting to remember more, aren't you?"

"Yes." He sat up, too. "I think I'll remember my name soon. I can almost feel it on the tip of my tongue."

"But where is Catherine now? Your wife...I mean that redheaded woman... What happened?"

"As soon as you left, she took me to her hotel. I didn't want to be alone with her, so I suggested we get a cup of coffee. When I realized that, whoever she was, she sure as hell wasn't my wife, I said I needed to use the men's room, and then I slipped out of the hotel. I got a taxi to the Institute and—"

"A taxi? How'd you pay him? You don't have any money."

"To tell the truth, I lifted her wallet."

"Ziggy!"

"How else was I supposed to get away? Anyhow, I wanted to know who she really was," he said reasonably. "But when I got here, no one would answer the door."

"No. Juan has strict instructions to never answer the door. You just have to force your way in if you want to see Grimly."

"Who's Juan?"

"Never mind."

"Well, it's lucky for me you were standing out on your balcony. I might have wound up breaking into your boss's room, otherwise." He kissed her shoulder and added, "Besides, I've always wanted to try climbing up to a lady's balcony."

"But Ziggy, who is this woman?"

He shrugged. "Beats me. According to the ID in her wallet, her name is Heather Jones. It doesn't mean anything to me."

"I don't understand. Why would someone pretend to be Catherine?" Her eyes widened. "Oh, my God."

He nodded. "To get their hands on—"

"The bunny!"

He frowned. "Well, yeah, the bunny, too. But *mostly*, to get their hands on *me*."

She leapt out of bed and retrieved the pink bunny from the balcony. "Just before you got here, I noticed that it feels funny. I'd never actually touched anything but its ears before."

"And I was so used to holding it, I never really—"

"There must be something inside the bunny!" she cried.

"God, you look great in that nightgown, Cherish. It makes my mouth water."

She blushed, noticing that he looked great when he was naked. But this was no time for lust. They had to find out the secret of the bunny's contents. "Stick to the subject," she chided.

There was a knife on her dinner tray. She picked it up and plunged it into the bunny's belly.

Ziggy winced. "Hey!" he said a moment later, springing out of the bed and joining Cherish in the moonlight.

"Good Lord!"

White powder spilled out of the bunny's belly and over Cherish's hands. An inspection of the gap in the fuzzy, pink material revealed that the knife had pierced a thick plastic wrapper.

"Drugs," Cherish said in amazement. "Someone was trying to smuggle drugs inside this bunny!"

"There must be half a kilo of the stuff in there," he said, watching the power spill onto the floor. A powerful vision flooded his mind. "Wait a minute!"

"You remember something?"

He looked at her in bewilderment. "Yeah. Thousands of bunnies. They were in packing crates, being loaded onto a ship for the United States."

Blinking at him in amazement, Cherish said, "You must have discovered a drug smuggling ring, Ziggy!"

He frowned. "Or maybe I was *part* of one," he said gloomily.

"Oh, nonsense. Despite your many character flaws, you're not a criminal."

"How do you know?"

"I just know," she insisted, reaching for her clothes.

His hand on her arm forestalled her. He studied her speculatively for a moment, then grinned. "Why, Dr. Love. I believe you're being reckless."

"Get dressed."

He ignored her command and pulled her against his naked body. "You meant it, didn't you?" he whispered.

She didn't have to ask what he meant. "Yes. God help me, but I meant it."

Their kiss was sweet and tender, and the gaze they exchanged made Cherish momentarily forget what they had just discovered.

"You realize we can't take this to the embassy," Ziggy remarked, moving away and reaching for his shorts.

She hesitated. "You think Waterson's involved? Why?"

"Didn't you notice how anxious that guy was to get you out of there? Didn't you see how green he turned when I gave the bunny to you?"

"No, I..."

"Tell me, was he the first person you talked to at the embassy?"

"No. When I called two days ago, the person I'd spoken to before said that Mr. Waterson, some kind of trade advisor, had decided to deal personally with my case."

"Why would a trade advisor concern himself with a missing person?"

Buttoning her blouse, Cherish said, "If Waterson is involved, then all he had to do was repeat back to me the information I had given them in the first place. And I believed him!"

"You had no way of knowing," he soothed, seeing the way she violently yanked her hair into a ponytail.

"I delivered you right into his paws. If he and the woman knew you'd been lost at sea, they probably thought you were dead. They never would have even known about you if it wasn't for me calling the embassy and telling them everything I knew about you!"

"Stop it," he ordered. "Any normal person would have done what you did."

"But how did you know something was wrong? Why did you give me the bunny?"

"It was a hunch. My head started pounding. It does that every time something reminds me of the night of the storm. I wanted to get you out of there as fast as possible. And as long as you were going, I decided to send the bunny with you." He sighed and sank upon the bed, fully dressed now. "To tell the truth, I was almost as scared at the thought that that overdressed woman might really be my wife."

She went still. "I was scared, too," she admitted softly.

"Cherish, whatever happens, I—"

"Whoever you are, Ziggy—" she interrupted briskly, pulling on her shoes "—you've sure gotten yourself into a hell of a mess. We don't even know who your enemies are."

Deciding personal matters would have to wait for the time being, he said, "Whoever they are, they mean business. I don't think I'd have turned up at that meeting Waterson promised you for tomorrow morning, Cherish. I have a feeling Heather Jones was supposed to lure me into a hotel room or safe house so they could find out how much I remember and then get rid of me.''

"I guess they couldn't very well do it right there in the embassy," she murmured, feeling sick.

"I wonder if anyone else at the embassy is involved.''

Cherish's stomach clenched when she realized how much danger Ziggy was still in. "We've got to talk to Grimly. Maybe he'll know what we should do. Come on.''

Just as she opened the bedroom door, they heard a tremendous racket coming from downstairs. Not even pausing to consider the wisdom of her actions, Cherish dashed down the staircase and made a beeline for Grimly's study.

Ziggy tackled her just before she got there. Winded, she rolled over and pushed at his chest as he lay heavily on top of her. "Stay here," he ordered in a fierce whisper, his face indistinct in the dark hallway.

"But—"

"Stay," he repeated. He rose stealthily to his feet and peered through the crack in the partially open door.

"Is that a gun?" Grimly demanded from inside his study. "Are you pointing a *gun* at me? What kind of a person are you?''

Cherish rolled her eyes. Trust Grimly to antagonize an armed assailant. She pushed herself to a sitting position and watched Ziggy, standing rigidly still in the shadows. She hoped he had a plan, because her mind had gone completely blank.

"Where's Ziggy Masterson?" It was Waterson's voice.

So *Masterson* was Ziggy's last name!

"Who?" Grimly demanded.

"Ziggy. The man who came to Belize City with Dr. Love," Waterson said impatiently.

"Oh, that addle-brained castaway who's made her lose nearly six full days of work during the past two weeks?" Grimly said. "How the devil should I know? I think she left him with some badly dressed redhead at the embassy." After a brief pause, he added snidely, "You, I presume, *madame?*"

A woman gasped in indignation. So Heather Jones was here, too! Cherish's heart sank when she heard a couple of men laughing as Waterson tried to shut them up. How many bad guys were there?

"Let's try this another way," Waterson said. "Ziggy gave Dr. Love something that belongs to us. If you'll just tell us where she is, so we can retrieve it—"

"I have no idea where she is."

"Don't give me that nonsense, Dr. Corridor! She said she was coming here."

"And she did, obviously. However, I cannot tolerate a colleague of her incompetence and unconscionable laziness. I fired her."

"You *what?*"

"Come now," Grimly said chidingly. "You've seen Cherish Love. Does she really look like a serious anthropologist to *you?*"

Cherish was astonished to realize that Grimly had, after all, noticed the way she looked. However, as long as she continued to work like a slave for wages that wouldn't support a frugal mouse, she had no doubt that he would continue to employ her while research funds lasted. If they both lived. The old curmudgeon was making a very creditable attempt to save Cherish's neck, but would the price be his own? She obviously couldn't allow that.

"Where did Dr. Love go?" Waterson asked skeptically.

"None of my business." After another pause, Grimly added, "But I believe she's rather partial to the Bay Club Hotel."

"The Bay Club?" Heather repeated. "I know that place."

"A woman of your sort undoubtedly would," Grimly said.

"Listen, you," Heather began angrily.

"I think you're lying to save her skin, Dr. Corridor," Waterson declared.

"You may think whatever you like, as often as you like, in whatever capacity is permitted to you by your Neanderthaloid mentality," Grimly said. "However, I absolutely forbid you to search the Institute. You've interrupted quite enough of my work as it is, and I am not about to neglect my paper on nineteenth-century Garifuna migrations for another moment, especially not on *your* behalf. I insist you leave at once. And I am prepared to support this insistence with physical force, if necessary."

"*I* have the gun," Waterson pointed out.

"I am unimpressed by your barbaric preening." Grimly sneered.

Cherish wished he wouldn't lay it on quite so thick. She looked up at Ziggy and had the horrible suspicion that he was trying not to laugh. She was about to reach out and tug on his ankle, wanted to get his attention so they could plan and launch a rescue attempt, when an enormous figure loomed out of the shadows behind him. She barely had time to scream before the hideous monster swung a large club at Ziggy's head.

Ziggy ducked quickly, but the club still managed to contact his skull with a nasty thud. The force of the blow sent him flying through the partially open door. Waterson whirled around and, seeing Ziggy stumbling toward him, fired the gun. Cherish screamed again when the bullet caught Ziggy in the shoulder and flung him backward. His body hit her as she came through the doorway, and they sprawled on the floor in a messy heap.

Heather screamed and pointed past Cherish. Juan, still armed with his club, stepped over Ziggy and Cherish and stalked toward Waterson. Grimly took advantage of the chaos and attacked one of Waterson's two henchmen. Waterson fired twice at Juan. Cherish thought he had hit his target, but Juan never even paused. He raised his club overhead and, a moment later, Waterson was lying unconscious on the ground. Juan then turned to deal with the next man.

"Ziggy! Ziggy!" Cherish cried, ripping off her blouse and wadding it into a ball. She pressed it hard against his fresh wound in an effort to staunch the flow of blood.

When all three of Heather's companions lay on the floor unconscious, she cast a desperate glance at the doorway, which Ziggy and Cherish were blocking, and then gave herself up.

"Very sensible," Grimly said. "I'm calling the police."

"Call an ambulance!" Cherish cried.

"Is he alive?" Grimly asked.

"Yes, but he's losing a lot of blood."

"Try to keep him conscious," Grimly advised. "And Juan, perhaps you could find something to put on the wound, as well as a shirt for Dr. Love?"

Juan nodded silently and stepped over Ziggy's body again.

"Ziggy, can you hear me?" Cherish asked, tears streaming down her face.

"Yes, I..." His head moved feebly and he licked his dry lips. "God, it hurts. Why are people always taking out their troubles on *me?*"

"Try not to talk—"

"No, let me give you my insurance information before I pass out. You know what hospitals are like," he said weakly. A moment later, his whole body tensed. "Oh, my God! Cherish, I *remember.*"

"What?"

"My name! I remember my name, and my social security number, and what color my car is, and the date of my father's birthday! I remember!"

He was breathing hard, making the blood flow faster. "That's wonderful, Ziggy," she said, her voice breaking with fear, "but try to stay calm. You don't want—"

"Tell the doctor, tell the ambassador, tell..."

"Yes, Ziggy."

"I'm Cornelius Ziegfeld Masterson III," he mumbled. "And tell that sonofabitch Waterson that I'm definitely going to press charges."

Eleven

There was so much to do. They checked Ziggy into the hospital and waited for the doctor's report after his surgery. Then they gave a statement—and the bunny—to the police. Before losing consciousness, Ziggy had given Cherish a telephone number in Florida to call. It turned out to be Clowance Masterson O'Grady's number—the academic sister whose name and face had skirted the edges of Ziggy's memory a few times. Although advanced pregnancy prevented Clowance from traveling, she assured Cherish that someone from the Masterson family, most of whom lived in New York, would leave for Belize immediately. To Cherish's disgust, Ziggy's family apparently had no idea that he'd been missing.

It was only after she hung up the phone that she registered the woman's married name: *O'Grady*. What precisely was Ziggy's connection with Michael O'Grady and the *Lusty Wench?* Was his brother-in-law a missing felon?

She wanted to go sit by his side then, but Grimly insisted she return to the Institute for a decent meal and some sleep.

"The doctor says he'll be fine," Grimly reminded her when she protested. "They're going to release him in a few days."

In the end, she did as Grimly ordered. She must have needed the rest, since she wound up sleeping until four o'clock the following afternoon. Grimly escorted her back to the hospital then, complaining the whole while about these many interruptions of his work.

"So your mysterious castaway is a Masterson, eh?" Grimly mused as they approached Ziggy's hospital room. "I thought the young rogue looked familiar, but it's hard to tell for sure when someone is wounded, unconscious and losing blood. At first I assumed I must know his face from a Wanted poster. I mean, what sort of person gets mixed up with gun-toting drug smugglers? However, I should have recognized the resemblance to his father."

"You know the Mastersons?" she asked incredulously, stopping in her tracks.

"Certainly. They financed two of my expeditions into the Amazon jungle."

"Really?" So Ziggy was right. There was money in his background.

"Yes. But then I permitted the boy's grandfather to accompany me on my next expedition, and for some reason, this seemed to infuriate Mr. Masterson. Ziggy would have been eighteen or nineteen. Yes! I remember now. He was expelled from Barrington University that same year. Something to do with an absurd prank involving a donkey in the library if I recall correctly."

"I can just imagine," she said wryly. "He's sort of mischievous. But who are the Mastersons? You make it sound like they have an awful lot of money."

"Stinking rich," Grimly said inelegantly. "Old money. There's a U.S. senator, a congressman and an ambassador in the extended family. Their holdings must be worth at least three or four hundred million dollars. Masterson Baking Products, the Masterson Hotels, the Masterson Foundation..." Always in search of research funding, Grimly possessed a surprisingly thorough knowledge of where the world's wealth was concentrated.

"Three or four hundred *million?*" Cherish's voice was shrill with shock. And to think she had doubted Ziggy's memories of driving a Porsche, owning an Arabian stallion and dining at Maxim's!

A mercenary expression crossed Grimly's face. "Perhaps now that we've saved Ziggy's miserable hide, his family will provide us with a little funding."

"Good Lord." Cherish felt dizzy. Somehow, the knowledge that her penniless, unidentified houseguest was heir to such immense wealth and position made him seem like a stranger. "I'm not sure I want to hear any more right now, Grimly." She paused outside the door to Ziggy's room. "Would you mind terribly if I saw him alone?"

"By all means. I'll inspect the premises. One never knows where a fascinating local custom will—"

"Yes, Grimly." She pushed open the door and went inside.

"There you are!" Ziggy exclaimed. He was sitting upright in bed, wearing a hospital gown and sporting an impressive set of dressings on his wounded shoulder. Despite what she had just learned, he looked reassuringly like his usual self: cocky, flirtatious and cheerful.

Only his unusual pallor and slow movements gave away how badly he'd been hurt last night.

"Ziggy." Her voice broke with relief. She stepped forward, wanting to hug him with all her might. Then she froze when a woman rose from a chair in the corner.

Sensing that Cherish wasn't going to give him any well-deserved kisses until he'd made the introductions, Ziggy waved carelessly at the astonishingly beautiful woman who had been sitting with him for the past two hours. "Catherine Masterson. Dr. Cherish Love."

Cherish looked from Ziggy, to the elegant, blue-eyed blonde, then back again. "Catherine?" she wailed.

Realizing the cause of her distress, he said quickly, "My sister."

"Your *sister?*"

"My *other* sister." Ziggy grinned. "Isn't that a kick in the pants? The watch was her gift to me on my thirtieth birthday."

"Your sister," she repeated, staring at the woman. Yes, now that she knew, she could see the resemblance. Ziggy and Catherine had the same aristocratic bone structure, the same full, sensual mouth and the same, unconscious air of command.

With a politely impersonal smile, Catherine stepped forward, clearly prepared to save the awkward moment. "How do you do?"

It was easy to guess now how Ziggy had learned to be so impeccably polite on those rare occasions when he attempted it. But Cherish wasn't in the mood to put up with such nonsense from his sister, too. "You're his sister?" she demanded heatedly. "What kind of a person are you? What kind of a family are you?"

"Uh, Cherish—" Ziggy began.

"How could you just let him disappear for two weeks without even looking for him? Are you aware he nearly died? *Twice?*"

Catherine never missed a beat. "I'm afraid we didn't know he was missing."

"He had no idea who he..." She ran out of steam. "What? How could you not know?"

"Perhaps you'd like to sit down, Dr. Love?"

"No!"

"Cherish. You'd better sit," Ziggy advised.

She sat. "Well?"

Catherine began. "Ziggy has—"

"That's *really* what people call him?"

Ziggy grunted. "With a name like Cornelius Ziegfeld Masterson III, what choice do I have?"

"Yes. I see what you mean," Cherish said.

"Maybe you'd better explain," Catherine told him.

"Our youngest sister, Clowance, got married about a year ago," he began. "Her husband is a treasure diver working out of Key West. My grandfather and I have taken an interest in the salvage operation and have been working down there with them—harvesting treasure, diving, working on the boats—"

"That explains the calluses on your hands, your tan, your muscles," Cherish said suddenly. "But what were you doing on the *Lusty Wench?*"

"I bought it off my brother-in-law—"

"He's not *our* brother-in-law," Catherine amended. "He's Clowance's brother-in-law."

"Right," Ziggy said. "Clowance's husband's brother is the guy who owned the *Lusty Wench,* the guy that jumped bail a few months back." He met Catherine's look defensively and said, "Hey! It's not *my* fault."

She looked away. He sighed and continued. "I bought the boat off him when it was clear he was going to need money for a good lawyer. I mean, I really liked the boat. I didn't know he'd use the money to disappear."

"Let's just hope he never reappears," Catherine said with distaste. "Anyhow, Ziggy neglected to transfer the title or do anything mundane like that. That's why you couldn't trace him even though you knew the name of the boat he'd been on."

"Oh, Ziggy." Cherish frowned at him.

"Don't you start, too," he warned. "I've already been listening to *her* say 'I told you so' for the past hour."

"But where's the *Wench* now?" Cherish asked. "Did she sink?"

"Waterson's people ditched her near some uninhabited cay off the coast of Mexico," Catherine said. "They hoped that if she was discovered, Ziggy would be presumed dead at sea."

"How do you know that?" Cherish asked.

"The police told me after they questioned Waterson. He and his—shall we say fiancée?—Heather Jones have agreed to cooperate with the police and implicate their associates," Catherine said.

"I can see you've been busy," Cherish remarked, recalling Ziggy's comments about Catherine. The woman didn't look like someone who'd been awakened in the middle of the night to learn her brother had been shot, and then flown to Belize and dealt with the local police, all in the space of twelve hours. Her linen dress wasn't even wrinkled.

"I've also hired a pilot to see if he can spot the, uh, *Lusty Wench* by air, Ziggy. I know you have a sentimental attachment to that trawler," Catherine said.

"I hope we can get it back," he replied.

"Why were you sailing off the coast of Belize? During a storm?" Cherish asked Ziggy, wondering why Catherine's *hair* wasn't even mussed. It was eerie.

"We wanted another boat for the treasure salvage, and we heard about one in Guatemala that we thought would be perfect. I sailed down to have a look at it, and I told Clowance and my grandfather that after I looked it over, I'd probably take my time about coming back. I wanted to explore a few of the smaller islands in the Caribbean. That's why it never occurred to any of them that I've been missing for two weeks."

"But how did you wind up in the middle of a drug-smuggling ring?"

"It was a complete accident. The owner of the boat I was looking at happened to be Waterson's Guatemalan partner in this smuggling operation. They were fabricating these awful pink bunnies by the thousands, stuffing them with cocaine and shipping them to the States."

"And Waterson was using his position as a trade advisor in Central America to clear the way for them," Catherine confirmed.

"I just happened to stumble across the real purpose of these shipments," Ziggy continued. "So, I stole one of the bunnies, thinking I'd turn it over to the authorities. But then the—gang, shall we say?—discovered I was onto them. I had to get out of Guatemala right away."

"So you took the bunny and put out to sea," Cherish guessed.

"I figured I'd contact the DEA or the Coast Guard as soon as I could."

"But the gang followed you."

Ziggy nodded. "They boarded the *Wench* just off the southern coast of Belize, tied me up and tried to radio their boss for instructions. But the storm was upon us by then. They couldn't get through on the radio, and we wandered way off course."

"Do you remember everything about that night now?" Cherish asked, searching his face carefully for signs of pain or distress.

His expression showed that it was an unpleasant but bearable memory now. "Most of it. Everything that happened to me after I jumped overboard is pretty dim, but I—"

"You jumped? On a night like that?"

"I didn't have much choice," he proclaimed. "There were four of them, armed with guns and knives, and they had just decided that their boss would probably prefer it if they simply killed me. I'm not a wimp—"

"I know you're not," she soothed.

"But there was no way I could take on four armed men. Particularly not after they'd beaten me to a pulp, tied me to a chair for twelve hours and left me sitting out in the middle of a tropical storm while they all got sick in the hold." He shook his head. "For a while there, I thought we'd *all* die."

He briefly described his escape—freeing one wrist from its bonds in time to struggle with an assailant armed with a knife, getting stabbed, cutting himself loose at last, grabbing the bunny and an old life preserver, jumping overboard and disappearing into the storm-tossed sea without knowing how far he was from land.

"I remember thinking I was dead meat," he murmured, a distant look on his face. "But I don't remember a thing about washing up on Indigo Beach."

Forgetting about Catherine, Cherish went to his side, took his hand and tenderly brushed his dark hair off his forehead. "Oh, Ziggy, how awful! No wonder your mind blocked out everything."

He gazed up at her with wide-eyed innocence. "I've just helped break up a drug smuggling ring, and been shot in the process—in the shoulder that was finally starting to heal, I might add. So don't you think I deserve a few really good kisses?"

"I think I should be leaving now," Catherine said tactfully. "I'm sure you can manage without me for the rest of the day, Ziggy."

"Bye, Catherine," he said, tugging on Cherish's arm, trying to pull her down onto the bed.

"Oh, by the way," Catherine added, pausing at the door. "I believe Grandfather will be arriving later today. Goodbye, Dr. Love. I imagine we'll meet again."

"Often," Ziggy assured her. "Now get lost."

As the door closed behind Catherine, Cherish said, "Your grandfather? Is he anything like *her*?"

"No. He's a great guy. You'll love him."

"I don't *dislike* her. It's just that she's . . ."

"I know what you mean. Come on, I've been very patient and well behaved."

"Up until a moment ago."

"So kiss me."

She did. Learning his true identity hadn't taken any of the magic out of his kiss. Quite the contrary.

"Again," he whispered, sliding his good arm around her neck.

"Wait a minute," she breathed. "There's so much I want to ask you. So much I don't know."

He rolled his eyes and flopped back against his pillow. Then he winced and rubbed his head. "Ow! That guy with the club sure packs a punch. How is he, by the way?"

"Juan? They pulled two bullets out of him." She shook her head in amazement. "He refused any anesthesia or painkillers, refused to even lie down for the operation, and looked insulted when Grimly suggested he take a few days off work.''

''There's definitely something to be said for sturdy peasant stock. And your boss? How's he?''

''Angry at you for interrupting his work, but otherwise unruffled. I don't think Waterson took into account how tough a man has to be to survive half a dozen trips down the Amazon. A little thing like a gun and three hoodlums wasn't going to ruin Grimly's night.''

His expression uncharacteristically serious, Ziggy said, ''I'm sorry, Cherish. I led them straight to you, giving you the bunny, like that. When I think of what they might have done—''

''Shh. You didn't know.''

''That's no excuse.''

''Okay, you unwittingly put me in danger, but you got shot for your trouble. So we're even. All right?''

He smiled. ''If you say so, Doc. How about another kiss? Or something more substantial. I think this bed can hold us both.''

''Ziggy,'' she said impatiently, ''do you realize who you are?''

''I do *now*.'' He looked smug. ''I *told* you I was rich. Really rich. I've even got money in Switzerland.''

''I can hardly take it in. It seems so strange.''

''Let me make it easy for you.'' He tugged at her hand and made her sit down beside him. ''I'm thirty-two years old. I'm single. I have a pretty wild past, but I've never done anything I'm ashamed of. I'm so good at cards because my grandfather taught me, the old rogue. I was kicked out of Barrington when I was nineteen, but I actually did graduate from college three years later. I only bothered because my father wouldn't let me near the family business until I had a degree.''

He paused and met her gaze. "What else can I tell you? Headwaiters everywhere know my name. All those memories about Maxim's, the Ritz, my red Porsche, and elegant French casinos were real, not fantasies. I probably thought of putting up a little hotel on Voodoo Caye because the idea was so familiar. I developed, built and opened the three hotels my family owns. I was thinking of opening up one in Key West, since that's where I seem to spend all my time lately, but all that has changed obviously.''

"It has?''

"Please," he said impatiently, "let's not have another one of those female conversations.''

"What are you talking about?''

"Are you going to pretend that you don't expect me to come back to Voodoo Caye?''

Her heart beat faster. "I . . . I . . .''

"Are you going to pretend you don't want to marry me? That you don't know I'm so in love with you I can't see straight? That you weren't miserable when you thought I was married to someone else? That—''

"Wait a minute, wait a minute.''

There was a knock at the door. Grimly entered the room a moment later. "Feeling better, are we?''

"Go away, Grimly," Cherish said. "Ziggy is asking me to marry him.''

"Yeah, go away, Grimly," Ziggy said, holding her gaze.

"Marry? Splendid! Just make sure you get a prenuptial agreement, Dr. Love, specifying the annual amount of our research funding. With cost-of-living increments, of course.''

"Go away, Grimly."

"This really is above and beyond the call of duty."
Grimly beamed. "I knew I was right to hire you, even if
you do look like a Las Vegas show girl."

Ziggy flung a pillow at the door as it closed. In a husky
voice, he said, "Are you going to pretend that you don't
know that from now on, I want it to be *my* job to make
sure men treat you with respect and keep their hands to
themselves?"

She didn't need a lot of time to think it through.
"Move over." Taking care not to hurt his shoulder, she
helped him slide sideways, then lay down beside him.

"Now this is more like it," he murmured.

Their mouths met, a gentle union of lips and tongues.
She felt her blood start to hum with that subtle song of
arousal that he had inspired in her from the very first. "I
can't wait till they let you out of here," she whispered.

His good hand moved to the fastening of her sensible
khaki shorts. "Why wait?"

She tried to push his hand away. "No, we can't. Not
here."

He pulled her zipper down. "Why not?"

"Someone . . ." She gasped and started breathing faster. "Someone might come in."

"They're nurses. They know what men and women do
together," he said reasonably, slipping his hand beneath
the elastic of her cotton panties. He kissed her again.

"Ohhh . . ." She pressed her forehead against his and
swallowed, feeling herself giving in. The touch of his
fingers, the heat of his body, the familiar affection in his
voice—how could she resist any of this? She certainly
couldn't contemplate living the rest of her life without it.
"But you're injured," she protested feebly, arching her
back when he caressed her breasts.

"I think you can work around that. Don't you?" He drew her hand down to his groin, which definitely wasn't affected by his wound.

She squeezed lightly, making him draw a sharp breath, then smiled as she studied his beloved features. After a moment, she said, "At least I know what to get you for a wedding present, even if you are the man who has everything."

He kissed her forehead. "What's that?"

"A decent bed for the cabin on Voodoo Caye."

He grinned, and his gray eyes sparkled with laughter. "Have I ever mentioned how smart you are?"

"Once or twice. Now tell me how much you love me."

And he did.

*   *   *   *   *

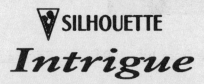

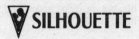

SILHOUETTE
Desire

COMING NEXT MONTH

BACHELOR BOYS: Men who don't know what hits them until the ring is on their finger!

WILD INNOCENCE Ann Major

Man of the Month and the third book in the Something Wild series

One night with Innocence Lescuer had cost Raven Wyatt two years of his life, but he had given Innocence a daughter so she had to set matters right...*if* he would let her.

YESTERDAY'S OUTLAW Raye Morgan

Mack Caine was a strictly "love 'em and leave 'em" type of guy until he heard that Taylor Taggert needed protection. She was the only woman who *might* be able to tame this bad boy!

SEVEN YEAR ITCH Peggy Moreland

Chase Morgan had spent seven years determined to forget his marriage to Kate McGinis! Why had she come to him now looking for explanations?

TWILIGHT MAN Karen Leabo

Faith Kimball couldn't be afraid of Jones Larabee after he saved her life, but she didn't understand why he was living a hermit's life deep in the swamp...

RICH GIRL, BAD BOY Audra Adams

Photographer Lucas Stratten wasn't proud of his latest job—to photograph heiress Alexandra Beck in a revealing situation for the tabloids—but he hadn't intended to end up snowbound alone with her!

BLACK LACE AND LINEN Susan Carroll

Laura's identical twin Chelsey had been pretending to be *her* and now she wanted Laura to deceive a very suspicious, very seductive Adam Barnhart.

COMING NEXT MONTH FROM

 **SILHOUETTE**

Sensation

A thrilling mix of passion, adventure, and drama

MACKENZIE'S MISSION Linda Howard
EXILE'S END Rachel Lee
THE HELL-RAISER Dallas Schulze
THE LOVE OF DUGAN MAGEE Linda Turner

Intrigue

*Danger, deception and desire—
new from Silhouette...*

NIGHT MOVES Nora Roberts
TIGER'S DEN Andrea Davidson
WHISTLEBLOWER Tess Gerritsen
MURDER BY THE BOOK Margaret St George

Special Edition

Satisfying romances packed with emotion

SALLY JANE GOT MARRIED Celeste Hamilton
HE'S MY SOLDIER BOY Lisa Jackson
WHEN STARS COLLIDE Patricia Coughlin
MARRY ME KATE Tracy Sinclair
WITH BABY IN MIND Arlene James
DENVER'S LADY Jennifer Mikels

4 SILHOUETTE DESIRES AND 2 GIFTS – yours absolutely FREE!

Provocative and sensual love stories for the sophisticated reader. A highly charged blend of forceful characters and daring storylines sets the scene for exciting and unpredictable encounters.

And to introduce this powerful series, we'd like you to accept our FREE offer of 4 books, a cuddly teddy and a MYSTERY gift without obligation. And, if you choose, go on to enjoy 6 Silhouette Desires every month for just £1.90 each.

Send the coupon below today to: Silhouette Reader Service, FREEPOST. PO Box 236, Croydon, Surrey CR9 9EL. (No stamp required).

YES! Please rush me 4 FREE Silhouette Desires and 2 FREE gifts! Please also reserve me a Reader Service subscription, which means I can look forward to receiving 6 brand new Desires for only £11.40 each month. Postage and packing is FREE and so is my monthly Newsletter. If I choose not to subscribe, I shall write to you within 10 days and still keep the FREE books and gifts. I may cancel or suspend my subscription at any time. I am over 18 years of age. Please write in BLOCK CAPITALS.

Ms/Mrs/Miss/Mr _____ EP76SD

Address _____

_____

_____ Postcode _____

Signature _____

Offer closes 31st October 1994. The right is reserved to refuse an application and to change the terms of this offer. One application per household. Offer not valid for current subscribers to this series. Valid in UK and Eire only. Readers overseas please write for details. Southern Africa write to IBS Private Bag X3010, Randburg 2125. You may be mailed with offers from other reputable companies as a result of this application. Please tick this box if you would prefer not to receive such offers. ☐

MAILING PREFERENCE SERVICE